Unit
Assessment

Includes Writing Prompts

Macmillan/McGraw-Hill

A

The *McGraw·Hill* Companies

 Macmillan/McGraw-Hill

Published by Macmillan/McGraw-Hill, of McGraw-Hill Education, a division of The McGraw-Hill Companies, Inc.,
Two Penn Plaza, New York, New York 10121.

Printed in the United States of America

1 2 3 4 5 6 7 8 9 024 13 12 11 10 09

Contents

Introduction to the Unit Assessment

The Unit Assessment is designed to measure your children's mastery of the specific skills taught in each unit of the *Treasures* reading program. The test questions use formats your children may encounter on standardized tests.

The Unit Assessments may test skills that are not evaluated on your state test but that are important skills in the *Treasures* program. Each Unit Assessment includes questions that cover the following areas:

- Listening Comprehension
- Reading Comprehension
- High-Frequency Words (Units 1–3)
- Vocabulary Strategies (Units 4–6)
- Literary Elements
- Text Features and Study Skills
- Grammar, Mechanics, and Usage
- Phonemic Awareness/Phonics
- Structural Analysis
- Writing (Units 4–6)

When scheduling the Unit Assessment, you will need to decide whether to administer it in one or more sessions. You may choose to give the first section of the Unit Assessment in one sitting and schedule the writing topic for another time.

How to Use the Unit Assessment

The Unit Assessment is given at the end of each unit, after the fifth week of instruction. Each assessment includes fiction and nonfiction passages and questions focusing on the main skills taught throughout the unit. There also is a writing prompt in Units 4–6 that gives children an opportunity to practice writing in a test situation. The type of writing is the same as the one focused on in the unit.

Sample Questions are included on **pages viii–ix** of this book to familiarize children with the format of standardized test items. They should be used before the first Unit Assessment; you may choose to review them with the children again before each test. Have children follow along as you read the instructions aloud. Allow children time to read the sample passage and then go over the questions and answers with them, answering any questions.

Anchor papers are provided for the three writing prompts. These samples illustrate the kinds of responses children are likely to write, as well as the most common kinds of errors found in children's writing at this grade level. These **Anchor Papers** can be found on **pages 172–183.**

Using the Results to Inform Instruction

Use the results of the Unit Assessment as a formative assessment tool to help monitor each child's progress. Information gathered by evaluating the results of this assessment also can be used to diagnose specific strengths and weaknesses of your children. If you use Unit Assessment scores to help determine report card grades, then you can consider the tests to be summative assessments as well.

The Unit Assessment scores should be one of multiple measures used to help make instructional decisions for the coming unit. Analyze which skills children have mastered and which ones require further reteaching. This information, along with the results of other assessments and your own observations, can be used to determine grouping and instructional decisions. Another way to use the Unit Assessment results is to compare them with the results of the corresponding Selection Tests and Weekly Assessments. Determine whether changes in instruction or additional small group support improved children's scores. The **Unit Reteaching and Intervention Charts** on **pages 184–189** will help you develop your reteaching plans.

Administering the Unit Assessment

Each Unit Assessment consists of 28 multiple-choice questions and two short-answer questions. The tests for Units 4–6 also include a writing prompt. The format of the test is the same for each unit. You may want to explain each section of the test to children the first time you administer it.

- For the multiple-choice questions, children should fill in the oval next to the answer they have chosen. (If you are using the separate Answer Sheet, direct students to fill in the circle for the answer they have chosen.) Remind children to make their marks dark and neat.

- For the short-answer questions, children should write their answers on the lines provided on the page. (If you are using the separate Answer Sheet, direct children to write their answers on the back of the Answer Sheet.)

- For the writing prompt, children should use the lined pages provided in the test booklet.

- The introductory pages that precede each Unit Assessment provide suggested scripts to follow when administering the test.

Answer Sheets can be found on **page 151** (Units 1–3) and **page 153** (Units 4–6) if you choose to use them.

The Answer Keys to score the tests can be found on **pages 156–167**.

General Procedures

Before the test: Distribute copies of the Unit Assessment and Answer Sheet, if you choose to use one.

Directions: Say: *Write your name and the date on the cover of your test booklet.* (If you are using the separate Answer Sheet, say: *Write your name and the date at the top of your Answer Sheet.*) When all children are finished, say: *Open the test booklet to page 2.*

During the test: Monitor children's test-taking behavior to make sure that each child is following the directions and writing responses in the correct places.

Answer questions about procedures and materials, but do not help children answer the test questions.

After the test: Before collecting the papers, make sure that children have written their names on the test booklet or at the top of the Answer Sheet.

Scoring the Unit Assessment

Using the Student Evaluation Charts

A Student Evaluation Chart follows each Unit Assessment. It lists all of the skills covered and the number of the question that assesses each skill.

- In the column labeled "Number Correct," fill in the point value for the questions answered correctly for each skill. Add the total number of points for correct responses and write the number for each subtest next to the total possible score.

- Add the scores for each skill (point value of the items answered correctly) to determine the total test score.

- To convert these raw test scores to percentages, divide the point value of the questions answered correctly by the total number of points. Example: A child earns 24 out of 32 possible points; 24 divided by 32 = .75 or 75%.

Multiple-choice questions are worth one point each. Short-answer questions are worth three points each. Writing prompts are worth four points.

Use the **Short-Answer Reading Rubric** on **page 155** to score the short-answer questions.

This program uses a focused holistic scoring system to score written compositions. Children's writing will be assessed in five domains: Focus and Coherence, Organization, Development of Ideas, Voice, and Conventions. The assigned score represents the child's command of the domains. Use the scoring criteria contained in the **Writing Rubrics** on **pages 168–171** to determine the overall level of the child's writing.

Evaluating the Scores

The primary focus of the Unit Assessments is to measure each child's progress toward mastery of each skill. Scores that fall below the 80th percentile suggest that children require additional instruction before mastery of that skill can be achieved. Evaluating the results of these assessments provides specific information about children's daily instructional needs. We recommend that you use these results for instructional planning and reteaching opportunities. Compare these results with your own observations of children's work and identify objectives that need further reinforcement. Incorporate these objectives into your instructional plans for the upcoming unit for individual, small group, or whole group instruction as indicated.

DIRECTIONS
Read the selection. Then answer the question.

Will It Rain?

Pat has her boots. She has her hat. She thinks it will rain. But the sun is out.

S-1 Why does Pat have her hat and her boots?

(A) It is hot.

(B) It may rain.

(C) She wants to get wet.

Revising and Editing Sample

DIRECTIONS

This is a story that Nat wrote. The story has mistakes. Read the story. Then answer the question.

I Am Nat

(1) my name is Nat. (2) I am six years old. (3) I ride the bus to school.

S-2 Which sentence needs a capital letter?

(A) Sentence 1

(B) Sentence 2

(C) Sentence 3

This Unit Assessment is designed to measure your children's mastery of the skills taught in the unit. The test assesses all of the following areas:

- Listening Comprehension
- Reading Comprehension
- High-Frequency Words
- Literary Elements
- Text Features and Study Skills
- Grammar, Mechanics, and Usage
- Phonemic Awareness/Phonics
- Structural Analysis

Listening Comprehension,
page 2

Say: *Listen while I read this story to you. You will be asked to answer three multiple-choice questions based on this story. Listen carefully. We will begin now.*

Paper Bag Puppet

Making your own puppet can be lots of fun. You will need a paper bag. First, use markers to make the puppet's eyes and mouth. Next, make the puppet's nose. Glue a button on the bag below the eyes. Then, glue yarn to the top of the bag. This will be the hair. Now your puppet is ready.

Now have children turn to page 2. Read the directions at the top of the page. Then say: *Listen carefully while I read each question. Listen to all three answer choices for each question. Then fill in the oval next to the answer you have chosen. Mark only one oval for each question. Mark your answers very carefully and make your marks dark and neat. When you have finished, put down your pencils and look at me.*

Have children answer questions 1 through 3 and stop on page 2.

Reading Comprehension; High-Frequency Words; Literary Elements; Text Features and Study Skills; Grammar, Mechanics, and Usage,
pages 3–17

Have children turn to page 3. *Say: You will now read some selections and answer some multiple-choice and short-answer questions. We will work through the test together. Read each selection carefully. Then we will read the questions that follow it. For each multiple-choice question, listen carefully as I read each answer choice. You will see that the lines in some selections are numbered. These numbers will help you find the lines and sentences you will need to answer the questions.*

After I read the answer choices, fill in the oval next to the answer you have chosen. Mark only one oval for each question. Mark your answers very carefully and make your marks dark and neat. Stop when you reach the stop sign and wait for me to tell you to go on. When you have finished, put down your pencils and look at me. You may begin now.

Have children answer questions 4–18 and stop on page 17.

Phonemic Awareness/Phonics; Structural Analysis
pages 18–20

Have children turn to page 18. Say: *I will now read you some questions. Listen very carefully. Then fill in the oval next to the best answer. Look at Number 19. I will say a word in parts: /l/ /i/ /p/. What word do you make when you put these sounds together? Listen to these answer choices:* lid, bib, lip. *Fill in the oval next to the picture that has the same sounds as /l/ /i/ /p/.*

Say: *Look at Number 20. Listen carefully as I say a word:* sand. *Now listen to these answer choices:* hand, crab, back. *Fill in the oval next to the picture that rhymes with* sand.

Say: *Look at Number 21. I will say a word:* cap. */k/ /a/ /p/. What is the middle sound in cap? Listen to these answer choices:* bat, mop, sink. *Mark the oval next to the picture that has the same middle sound as* cap.

Say: *I will say the name of each picture. After I say the name, read the three answer choices. Fill in the oval next to the word that names the picture. Look at Number 22. I will say the name of the picture now. "Pan." "Pan." Read the three answer choices and mark the answer next to the word "pan."*

Continue in the same way through page 19.

Number 23: hat; *Number 24:* pig; *Number 25:* flag; *Number 26:* hand; *Number 27:* sink.

For numbers 28 through 30, have students turn to page 20. Say: *Listen carefully while I read each question and all three answer choices for each question. Then fill in the oval next to the answer you have chosen. Mark only one oval for each question. Mark your answers very carefully and make your marks dark and neat. When you have finished, put down your pencils and look at me.*

Have children answer questions 28 through 30 and stop on page 20.

© Macmillan/McGraw-Hill

Student Name _____

Date _____

Unit
Assessment

TESTED SKILLS AND STRATEGIES

- **Listening Comprehension**
- **Reading Comprehension**
- **High-Frequency Words**
- **Literary Elements**
- **Text Features and Study Skills**
- **Grammar, Mechanics, and Usage**
- **Phonemic Awareness/Phonics**
- **Structural Analysis**

Macmillan/McGraw-Hill

DIRECTIONS

Listen as your teacher reads the selection. Then answer each question.

1 The author wrote "Paper Bag Puppet" to tell you —

   (A) how to buy a puppet

   (B) a story about a puppet

   (C) how to make a puppet

2 The last thing you do to make a puppet is —

   (A) make the eyes

   (B) put yarn on the bag

   (C) put your hand in the bag

3 To make a puppet you _____ need a paper bag.

   (A) willl

   (B) will

   (C) wil

STOP

DIRECTIONS
Read the selection. Then answer each question.

Flip Can Play!

Flip can jump.

© Macmillan/McGraw-Hill

Flip can tag.

GO ON ▶

Unit Assessment

Flip is too big.
He can not go in.

GO ON

Page 5

Flip digs very fast.

Page 6

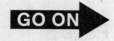

Unit Assessment

Now Flip can play!

Page 7

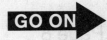

4 Look at the chart.

Character	What He Does
Flip	

What goes in the empty box?

    Ⓐ Digs

    Ⓑ Rides

    Ⓒ Naps

5 Flip digs ___ fast.

    Ⓐ now

    Ⓑ jump

    Ⓒ very

6 What is Flip's problem?

    Ⓐ He can't dig.

    Ⓑ He can't get in.

    Ⓒ He can't jump.

7 Flip can play —

    A too

    B very

    C jump

8 What does Flip do first?

    A Digs

    B Jumps

    C Tags

9 What can Flip do?

_____

_____

_____

_____

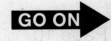

DIRECTIONS
Read the poem. Then answer the question.

Dreaming

1   I am twenty feet tall,

2   My brother looks so small!

3   I hear someone calling me:

4   My mom is who I see.

5   Wake up, you sleepy head!

6   Time for school! Get out of bed!

---

10 Which words in this poem are rhyming words?

A get and bed

B me and my

C tall and small

STOP

Student Name _____

DIRECTIONS
Answer each question.

11 Look at the picture.

Ducks like to —

Ⓐ swim in the pond

Ⓑ climb trees

Ⓒ collect nuts

Student Name _____

12 Look at the labels.

Feathers
Wings
Eyes
Beak

Claws

The bird has only one —

A feather

B wing

C beak

13 Look at the list.

What should you do in school?

A Run in place

B Shout

C Take turns

School Rules

1. walk in line
2. raise your hand
3. take turns

GO ON ▶

14 Look at the book cover.

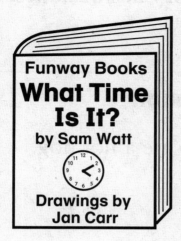

The name of the author is —

(A) Jann Carr

(B) Sam Watt

(C) Funway Books

STOP

DIRECTIONS

This is a story that Sally wrote. The story has mistakes. Read the story. Then answer the questions.

A Hot Dog for Hannah

(1) Did Hannah eat lunch? (2) She ate a hot dog.

(3) Hot dogs I love to eat!

GO ON ➡

15 Which sentence is a statement?

(A) Sentence 1

(B) Sentence 2

(C) Sentence 3

16 What is the **BEST** way to write sentence 3?

(A) I hot dogs love to eat!

(B) I to eat and love hot dogs!

(C) I love to eat hot dogs!

GO ON ➡

DIRECTIONS

This is a story that Jim wrote. The story has mistakes. Read the story. Then answer the questions.

My Friend Kim

(1) It is fun to play with Kim. (2) She can jump and flip (3) can kim come play with me?

17 What is the **BEST** way to write sentence 3?

(A) Can Kim come play with me?

(B) can KIM come play with me?

(C) Can kim come play with me?

18 Which sentence needs a period?

(A) Sentence 1

(B) Sentence 2

(C) Sentence 3

STOP

Listen while your teacher reads the directions.

19 (A)    (B)    (C)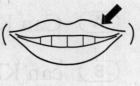

20 (A) 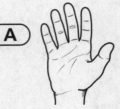   (B)    (C)

21 (A)    (B)    (C)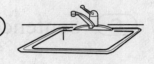

Choose the word that names the picture.

22    (A) pin

(B) pan

(C) man

GO ON ➡

Student Name _____

23
- Ⓐ hit
- Ⓑ hat
- Ⓒ mat

24
- Ⓐ pig
- Ⓑ big
- Ⓒ bag

25
- Ⓐ clip
- Ⓑ flap
- Ⓒ flag

26
- Ⓐ bank
- Ⓑ hand
- Ⓒ band

27
- Ⓐ sink
- Ⓑ sit
- Ⓒ sank

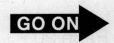

Page 19

Answer these questions.

28 Kim sees ___ at the store.

    Ⓐ cat

    Ⓑ cat's

    Ⓒ cats

29 The cat ___ to Kim.

    Ⓐ run

    Ⓑ runs

    Ⓒ running

30 Kim's cat ran up the —

    Ⓐ hil

    Ⓑ hill

    Ⓒ hill's

STOP

Student Name _____

Grade 1 • Unit 1
Student Evaluation Chart

Tested Skills	Number Correct	Percent Correct
Listening Comprehension: *Author's Purpose*, 1; *Sequence*, 2; *Double Final Consonants*, 3	/3	%
Reading Comprehension: *Character*, 4; *Plot*, 6; *Sequence*, 8	/3	%
Short answer: *Character*, 9	/3	%
High-Frequency Words: very, 5; too, 7	/2	%
Literary Elements: *Identify Rhyme*, 10	/1	%
Text Features and Study Skills: *Photographs*, 11; *Labels*, 12; *Lists*, 13; *Book Parts*, 14	/4	%
Grammar, Mechanics, and Usage: *Sentences*, 15; *Word Order*, 16; *Capitalization*, 17; *Punctuation*, 18	/4	%
Phonemic Awareness: *Phoneme Blending*, 19; *Identify Rhyme*, 20; *Phoneme Isolation*, 21	/3	%
Phonics: *Short a*, 22, 23; *Short i*, 24; *Consonant Blends*, 25, 26, 27	/6	%
Structural Analysis: *Inflectional Ending s*, 28, 29; *Double Final Consonants*, 30	/3	%
Total Unit Test Score	/32	%

This Unit Assessment is designed to measure your children's mastery of the skills taught in the unit. The test assesses all of the following areas:

- Listening Comprehension
- Reading Comprehension
- High-Frequency Words
- Literary Elements
- Text Features and Study Skills
- Grammar, Mechanics, and Usage
- Phonemic Awareness/Phonics
- Structural Analysis

Listening Comprehension,
page 2

Say: *Listen while I read this story to you. You will be asked to answer three multiple-choice questions based on this story. Listen carefully. We will begin now.*

One Little Pig

One day a pig built a house of sticks. Just as he finished, a wolf came by. The wolf huffed and puffed and blew the house in.

"What fun!" laughed the wolf.

"Wolf," said the pig, "Why did you blow my house down?"

"I just love to huff and puff," said the wolf.

"Wait just one minute," said the pig.

He looked under a pile of sticks and found a packet of one hundred balloons. He gave them to the wolf.

"This is just what I always wanted!" said the wolf. He blew up a red balloon. "What fun!" he laughed. Then he ran off and never bothered the little pig again.

Now have children turn to page 2. Read the directions at the top of the page. Then say: *Listen carefully while I read each question. Listen to all three answer choices for each question. Then fill in the oval next to the answer you have chosen. Mark only one oval for each question. Make your marks dark and neat. When you have finished, put down your pencils and look at me.*

Have children answer questions 1 through 3 and stop on page 2.

Reading Comprehension; High-Frequency Words; Literary Elements; Text Features and Study Skills; Grammar, Mechanics, and Usage,
pages 3–17

Have children turn to page 3. Say: *You will now read some selections and answer some multiple-choice and short-answer questions. We will work through the test together. Read each selection carefully. Then we will read the questions that follow it. For each multiple-choice question, listen carefully as I read each answer choice. You will see that the lines in the selections are numbered. These numbers will help you find the lines and sentences you will need to answer the questions.*

After I read the answer choices, fill in the oval next to the answer you have chosen. Mark only one oval for each question. Mark your answers very carefully and make your marks dark and neat. Stop when you reach the stop sign and wait for me to tell you to go on. When you have finished, put down your pencils and look at me. You may begin now.

Have children answer questions 4–18 and stop on page 17.

Phonemic Awareness/Phonics; Structural Analysis,
pages 18–20

Have children turn to page 18. Say: *I will now read you some questions. Listen very carefully. Then fill in the oval next to the best answer. Look at Number 19. I will say a word:* fun. *Listen to the middle sound in the word* fun. *Listen to these answer choices:* fan, sun, dog. *Fill in the oval next to the picture that has the same middle sound as* fun.

Say: *Look at Number 20. I will say a word in parts: /n/ /e/ /k/. What word do you make when you blend these sounds together? Listen to these answer choices:* neck, tack, mint. *Fill in the oval next to the picture that has the same sounds as /n/ /e/ /k/.*

Say: *Look at Number 21. I will say a word in parts: /l/ /o/ /k/. What word do you make when you blend these sounds together? Listen to these answer choices:* lick, rock, lock. *Fill in the oval next to the picture that has the same sounds as /l/ /o/ /k/.*

Say: *I will say the name of each picture. After I say the name, read the three answer choices. Fill in the oval next to the word that names the picture. Look at Number 22. I will say the name of the picture now. "Sock." "Sock." Read the three answer choices and mark the answer next to the word "sock."*

Continue in the same way through page 19.

Number 23: bed; Number 24: bug; Number 25: fish; Number 26: stop; Number 27: trap.

For Numbers 28 through 30, Have students turn to page 20. Say: *Listen carefully while I read each question and all three answer choices for each question. Then fill in the oval next to the answer you have chosen. Mark only one oval for each question. Mark your answers very carefully and make your marks dark and neat. When you have finished, put down your pencils and look at me.*

Have children answer questions 28 through 30 and stop on page 20.

Student Name _____

Date _____

Unit
Assessment
TESTED SKILLS AND STRATEGIES

- **Listening Comprehension**
- **Reading Comprehension**
- **High-Frequency Words**
- **Literary Elements**
- **Text Features and Study Skills**
- **Grammar, Mechanics, and Usage**
- **Phonemic Awareness/Phonics**
- **Structural Analysis**

Mc Graw Hill Macmillan/McGraw-Hill

DIRECTIONS

Listen as your teacher reads the selection. Then answer each question.

1 What happens first in the story?

    (A) The wolf blows the house in.

    (B) A pig built a house.

    (C) The pig gave the wolf a balloon.

2 What is the pig's problem?

    (A) The wolf has too many balloons.

    (B) The pig built a house of sticks.

    (C) The wolf blew his house in.

3 "This is just what I always —"

    (A) wanting

    (B) wanted

    (C) wants

Page 2

STOP

Dogs can do many tricks. They can jump. They can fetch.

Page 3

GO ON ➤

Some dogs go to school to learn tricks. They learn to sit and come.

This pup's trick is very good. She wants to eat. She sits up.

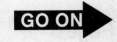

This dog is fast. He puts on a show. He jumps over the bricks stacked together.

Page 6

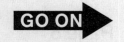

This dog can not do tricks. Her leg is hurt, but she can lick.

Page 7

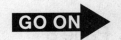

4 Look at the chart.

| Dogs can fetch. | Dogs jump over bricks. | Dogs sit and come. |

What main idea goes in the empty box?

(A) Dogs do tricks.

(B) Dogs are funny.

(C) All kinds of dogs.

5 _____ dogs go to school.

(A) Eat

(B) Want

(C) Some

6 What do dogs learn at school?

(A) They learn to sit and come.

(B) They learn to lick.

(C) They learn to eat.

© Macmillan/McGraw-Hill

Page 8

7 Dogs can do _____ fun things.

    Ⓐ they

    Ⓑ many

    Ⓒ show

8 When the pup wants to eat, she —

    Ⓐ fetches

    Ⓑ barks

    Ⓒ sits up

9 What dog tricks does the story talk about?

_____

_____

_____

_____

GO ON

DIRECTIONS
Read the poem. Then answer the question.

What Fun We'll Have

1   Let's dance and sing,

2   Let's run and play.

3   What fun we'll have,

4   On my birthday!

10 How many beats are there in each line of this poem?

(A) 2

(B) 3

(C) 4

Unit Assessment

Student Name _____

DIRECTIONS
Answer each question.

11 Look at the diagram.

What is at the top of the daisy?

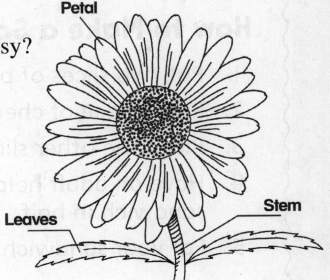

(A) Stem

(B) Leaves

(C) Petals

12 Read these dictionary entries.

> **Beak:** the hard part of a bird's mouth
>
> **Bean:** a seed that people can eat
>
> **Bear:** a large furry animal with sharp claws

Which word has a meaning that tells about food?

(A) Beak

(B) Bean

(C) Bear

13 Read these directions.

How to Make a Sandwich

1. Put two slices of bread on a plate.
2. Put a piece of cheese on one slice.
3. Place the other slice on top.
4. Have an adult help you cut the sandwich in half.
5. Eat your sandwich!

What do you do right after you put on the cheese?

(A) Put two slices of bread on a plate.

(B) Put the other slice on top.

(C) Have an adult help you cut the sandwich.

Page 12

GO ON ➡

14 Look at the picture.

What is the boy having for lunch?

Ⓐ Soup, apple, milk

Ⓑ Sandwich, banana, milk

Ⓒ Sandwich, apple, milk

STOP

DIRECTIONS

This is a story that Sara wrote. The story has mistakes. Read the story. Then answer the questions.

My School Play

(1) The school play is next monday. (2) Tomas will be a rabbit. (3) Many child are in it.

15 What is the **BEST** way to write sentence 1?

    Ⓐ The school play is next Monday.

    Ⓑ The School play is next monday.

    Ⓒ The school Play is next monday.

16 What is the **BEST** way to write sentence 3?

    Ⓐ Many childrens are in it.

    Ⓑ Many childs are in it.

    Ⓒ Many children are in it.

GO ON

DIRECTIONS

This is a story that Tim wrote. The story has mistakes. Read the story. Then answer the questions.

The Duck Pond

(1) I saw three duckees at the park today. (2) My moms took a picture of them. (3) We fed them, too!

Page 16

17 What is the **BEST** way to write sentence 1?

(A) I saw three duck at the park today.

(B) I saw three ducks at the park today.

(C) I saw three duckes at the park today.

18 What is the **BEST** way to write sentence 2?

(A) My mom took a picture of them.

(B) My momms took a picture of them.

(C) My momes took a picture of them.

Listen while your teacher reads the directions.

19 (A) 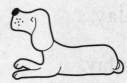 (B)   (C)

20 (A)  (B)   (C)

21 (A)  (B)   (C)

Choose the word that names the picture.

22

(A) sick

(B) sack

(C) sock

GO ON ➡

23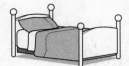
- (A) bid
- (B) bad
- (C) bed

24
- (A) beg
- (B) bog
- (C) bug

25
- (A) fist
- (B) fish
- (C) find

26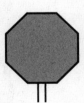
- (A) stop
- (B) flap
- (C) stick

27
- (A) trap
- (B) trip
- (C) grab

Page 19

Answer these questions.

28 What is another way to write the words can not?

    (**A**) ca'nt

    (**B**) can't

    (**C**) couldn't

29 The dog is _____ over a plank.

    (**A**) jumps

    (**B**) jumped

    (**C**) jumping

30 _____ a good dog.

    (**A**) Hes

    (**B**) He's

    (**C**) Hes'

STOP

Grade 1 • Unit 2

Student Evaluation Chart

Tested Skills	Number Correct	Percent Correct
Listening Comprehension: *Sequence, 1; Plot, 2; Inflectional Endings, 3*	/3	%
Reading Comprehension: *Main Idea and Details, 4, 6, 8*	/3	%
Short answer: *Main Idea and Details, 9*	/3	%
High-Frequency Words: some, 5; many, 7	/2	%
Literary Elements: *Rhythm, 10*	/1	%
Text Features and Study Skills: *Diagram, 11; Dictionary 12; Follow Directions, 13; Use Photographs, 14*	/4	%
Grammar, Mechanics, and Usage: *Plural Nouns, 16, 17, 18; Proper Nouns, 15*	/4	%
Phonemic Awareness: *Phoneme Isolation, 19; Phoneme Blending, 20, 21*	/3	%
Phonics: *Short o, 22; Short e, 23; Short u, 24; Consonant Digraphs, 25; Consonant Blends 26, 27*	/6	%
Structural Analysis: *Contractions, 28, 30; Inflectional Endings, 29*	/3	%
Total Unit Test Score	**/32**	**%**

This Unit Assessment is designed to measure your children's mastery of the skills taught in the unit. The test assesses all of the following areas:

- Listening Comprehension
- Reading Comprehension
- High-Frequency Words
- Literary Elements
- Text Features and Study Skills
- Grammar, Mechanics, and Usage
- Phonemic Awareness/Phonics
- Structural Analysis

Listening Comprehension, page 2

Say: *Listen while I read this story to you. You will be asked to answer three multiple-choice questions based on this story. Listen carefully. We will begin now.*

Tree Houses

Many animals can live in a hole in a tree. A mother woodpecker can use a little hole in a tree. She finds a small hole and makes it larger. She lays her eggs in the hole. It is her nest. Her babies start eating and growing stronger. Then the family flies away. Some bugs will dig into the wood. They eat small bits of the tree. They make the hole bigger. Then a tree squirrel moves in. The squirrel puts grass and leaves into the hole to make a soft nest. After the squirrel moves away, the hole may become a home for another animal.

Now have children turn to page 2. Read the directions at the top of the page. Then say: *Listen carefully while I read each question. Listen to all three answer choices for each question. Then fill in the oval next to the answer you have chosen. Mark only one oval for each question. Make your marks dark and neat. When you have finished, put down your pencils and look at me.*

Have children answer questions 1 through 3 and stop on page 2.

Now have children turn to page 2. Then say: *Listen carefully while I read each question. Listen to all three answer choices for each question. Then fill in the oval next to the answer you have chosen. Mark only one oval for each question. Make your marks dark and neat. When you have finished, put down your pencils and look at me.*

Have children answer questions 1 through 3 and stop on page 2.

Reading Comprehension; High-Frequency Words; Literary Elements; Text Features and Study Skills; Grammar, Mechanics, and Usage,

pages 3–17

Have children turn to page 3. Say: *You will now read some selections and answer some multiple-choice and short-answer questions. We will work through the test together. Read each selection carefully. Then we will read the questions that follow it. For each multiple-choice question, listen carefully as I read each answer choice. You will see that the lines in some selections are numbered.*

Grade 1 • Unit 3

These numbers will help you find the lines or sentences you will need to answer the questions. For each multiple-choice question read each answer choice. Then fill in the oval next to the answer you have chosen. Mark only one oval for each question. Mark your answers very carefully and make your marks dark and neat. Stop when you reach the stop sign and wait for me to tell you to go on. When you have finished, put down your pencils and look at me. You may begin now.

Have children answer questions 4–18 and stop on page 17.

Phonemic Awareness/Phonics; Structural Analysis,
pages 18–20

Have children turn to page 18. Say: I will now read you some questions. Listen very carefully. Then fill in the oval next to the best answer. Look at Number 19. I will say a word with five sounds: struck /s/ /t/ /r/ /u/ /k/. Take away the first sound /s/ from the word struck. What new word did you make? Listen to these answer choices: ring, wing, truck.

Say: Look at Number 20. I will say a word in parts: /ch/ /i/ /k/. What word do you make when you blend these sounds together? Listen to these answer choices: chin, chick, stick. Fill in the oval next to the picture that has the same sounds as /ch/ /i/ /k/.

Say: Look at Number 21. I will say a word: bike, /b/ /i/ /k/. Listen to these answer choices: kite, bib, bath. Fill in the oval next to the picture that has the same middle sounds as bike.

Say: I will say the name of each picture. After I say the name, read the three answer choices. Fill in the oval next to the word that names the picture. Look at Number 22. I will say the name

of the picture now. "Cane." "Cane." Read the three answer choices and mark the answer next to the word "Cane."

Continue in the same way through page 19.

Number 23: bike; Number 24: spring; Number 25: chimp; Number 26: knot; Number 27: stripes.

For Numbers 28 through 30, Have students turn to page 20. Say: Listen carefully while I read each question and all three answer choices for each question. Then fill in the oval next to the answer you have chosen. Mark only one oval for each question. Mark your answers very carefully and make your marks dark and neat. When you have finished, put down your pencils and look at me.

Have children answer questions 28 through 30 and stop on page 20.

Student Name _____

Date _____

Unit Assessment

TESTED SKILLS AND STRATEGIES

- **Listening Comprehension**
- **Reading Comprehension**
- **High-Frequency Words**
- **Literary Elements**
- **Text Features and Study Skills**
- **Grammar, Mechanics, and Usage**
- **Phonemic Awareness/Phonics**
- **Structural Analysis**

Mc Graw Hill **Macmillan/McGraw-Hill**

DIRECTIONS
Listen as your teacher reads the selection. Then answer each question.

1 What is this story mostly about?

    (A) How birds eat bugs

    (B) How holes get bigger

    (C) How animals use holes in trees

2 How are woodpeckers and tree squirrels alike?

    (A) They make nests using grasses and leaves.

    (B) They make nests inside of trees.

    (C) They make holes in trees bigger.

3 The babies start —

    (A) eating

    (B) eat

    (C) eaten

STOP

Spike Takes the Cake

It was Jake's big day. Now he was six. Some boys and girls from school came over to play. "Let's have fun!" said Jake.

Jake's dog Spike was there, too. Spike liked Jake's friends. "Yip!" said Spike.

GO ON ➡

The boys and girls jumped rope. "Look at us!" they called. Spike wanted to jump rope, too. He yipped. He jumped up. But the kids did not let him play.

Page 4

GO ON ➡

Next Jake and his pals went for a swim. They jumped and skipped in the yard. Spike looked at them play. He wanted to play, too.

Then the kids played more games. Jake had to find the place for the tail. Spike wanted to help him. "Yip!" said Spike. But Jake did not hear him.

GO ON

Then the kids ate snacks together. Spike wanted to eat, too. Jake had a chunk of cake in his hand. Spike had a bite. "Yum!" said Spike. Jake looked at Spike and smiled. Now Spike was having fun, too.

Page 7

GO ON ▶

4 On page 4, which words help you to know that Spike wanted to play?

    (A) Spike wanted to jump rope, too.

    (B) The boys and girls jumped rope.

    (C) But the kids did not let him play.

5 Jake's friends are at the party. Spike is _____, too.

    (A) friend

    (B) there

    (C) from

6 Why does Spike yip and jump?

    (A) He is afraid.

    (B) He wants to play.

    (C) He wants to go inside.

GO ON ➡

7 The kids played _____ games.

  (A) school

  (B) call

  (C) more

8 What happens in the middle of the story?

  (A) The kids play.

  (B) The kids come over.

  (C) Spike eats cake.

9 What is Spike's problem?

_____

_____

_____

GO ON

Student Name _____

DIRECTIONS
Read the poem. Then answer the question.

Silver Dollar

1   I held it in my hand,
2   It had sparkle and shine,
3   It was heavy and round,
4   All silver and all mine.

10 What does the word <u>shine</u> tell you about a silver dollar?

(A) It is bright.

(B) It is hard to hold.

(C) It is larger than a nickel.

Page 10

Unit Assessment

DIRECTIONS
Answer each question.

11 Look at the floor plan.

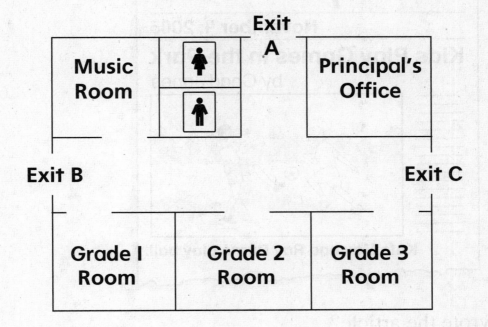

Which exit is the closest to the Grade 1 room?

(A) Exit A

(B) Exit B

(C) Exit C

12 Look at the newspaper.

Today's News

November 4, 2005

Kids Play Games in the Park

by Chad Jones

Kate May and Ray Burns play ball.

Who wrote the article?

- **A** Chad Jones
- **B** Kate May
- **C** Ray Burns

GO ON

Page 12

13 Look at the chart.

What is your favorite color?	
Color	**Number of Children**
Red	卌 I
Blue	卌 IIII
Green	卌 II
Yellow	卌

Which color do most of the children like best?

(A) Blue

(B) Green

(C) Yellow

14 Look at the sign.

What does the sign tell you?

(A) Stop here

(B) Cross the street here

(C) Do not enter

STOP

DIRECTIONS

This is a story that Nick wrote. The story has mistakes.
Read the story. Then answer the questions.

My Friend Dan

(1) I rides to school with Dan. (2) Dan lives next door.
(3) We is in first grade.

© Macmillan/McGraw-Hill

15 Which sentence uses the correct verb?

   (A) Sentence 1

   (B) Sentence 2

   (C) Sentence 3

16 What is the **BEST** way to write sentence 3?

   (A) Were is in first grade.

   (B) I are in first grade.

   (C) We are in first grade.

GO ON

This is a story that Anne wrote. The story has mistakes.
Read the story. Then answer the questions.

Dancing Friends

(1) I take dancing lessons. (2) My friend Tim dancer
with me. (3) Tim stay with us last year.

17 What is the **BEST** way to write sentence 2?

     (A) My friend Tim dance with me.

     (B) My friend Tim dances with me.

     (C) My friend Tim dancing with me.

18 What is the **BEST** way to write sentence 3?

     (A) Tim stay with us last year.

     (B) Tim stays with us last year.

     (C) Tim stayed with us last year.

STOP

Student Name _____

Listen while your teacher reads the directions.

19 (A)  (B)  (C)

20 (A)  (B)  (C)

21 (A) 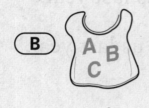 (B) (C)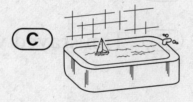

Choose the word that names the picture.

22  (A) can

(B) cane

(C) cone

23

- Ⓐ bite
- Ⓑ bike
- Ⓒ bit

24

- Ⓐ swing
- Ⓑ spring
- Ⓒ ring

25

- Ⓐ chimp
- Ⓑ shrimp
- Ⓒ champ

26

- Ⓐ not
- Ⓑ knot
- Ⓒ knit

27

- Ⓐ stripes
- Ⓑ sprints
- Ⓒ strings

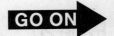

Page 19

Answer these questions.

28 Spike _____ the children when they play.

(A) watch

(B) watcher

(C) watches

29 Jake _____ games in the yard.

(A) play

(B) playing

(C) played

30 He _____ and ran.

(A) jumped

(B) jumping

(C) jumps

STOP

Student Name _____

Grade 1 • Unit 3
Student Evaluation Chart

Tested Skills	Number Correct	Percent Correct
Listening Comprehension: *Main Idea and Details, 1; Compare and Contrast, 2; Inflectional Endings, 3*	/3	%
Reading Comprehension: *Make and Confirm Predictions, 4; Character, 6; Sequence, 8*	/3	%
Short answer: *Plot, 9*	/3	%
High-Frequency Words: there, 5; more, 7	/2	%
Literary Elements: *Sensory Language, 10*	/1	%
Text Features and Study Skills: *Floor Plan, 11; Newspapers and Periodicals, 12; Chart, 13; Signs and Symbols, 14*	/4	%
Grammar, Mechanics, and Usage: *Present-Tense Verbs, 15, 16, 17; Past-Tense Verbs, 18*	/4	%
Phonemic Awareness: *Phoneme Deletion, 19; Phoneme Blending, 20; Phoneme Isolation, 21*	/3	%
Phonics: *Long a, 22; Long i, 23; Three-Letter Blends, 24, 27; Consonant Digraphs, 25, 26*	/6	%
Structural Analysis: *Inflectional Endings, 28, 29, 30*	/3	%
Total Unit Test Score	/32	%

Grade 1 • Unit 4

This Unit Assessment is designed to measure your children's mastery of the skills taught in the unit. The test assesses all of the following areas:

- Listening Comprehension
- Reading Comprehension
- Vocabulary Strategies
- Literary Elements
- Text Features and Study Skills
- Grammar, Mechanics, and Usage
- Phonemic Awareness/Phonics
- Structural Analysis
- Writing

Listening Comprehension,
page 2

Say: *Listen while I read this story to you. You will be asked to answer three multiple-choice questions based on this story. Listen carefully. We will begin now.*

Ants Save The Day

Charlie was upset. His class was hosting a bake sale to raise money for a field trip. Charlie didn't have anything to bring. He told his sister about the problem. She said that she would help him after she finished her homework, but he couldn't wait any longer.

Then Charlie had an idea. "What if I make ants on a log?" First, he took pieces of celery and laid them out. Next, he filled each piece with peanut butter. Now he had logs. Finally he topped each log with four raisins. The raisins were ants. He made so many he could barely carry them all. His teacher charged 75 cents for each one. They all sold, and the class made enough for their trip.

When Charlie got home that afternoon, his sister apologized for not helping. Charlie said, "That's okay, I had fun doing it myself."

Now have children turn to page 2. Read the directions at the top of the page. Then say: *Listen carefully while I read each question. Listen to all three answer choices for each question. Then fill in the oval next to the answer you have chosen. Mark only one oval for each question. Make your marks dark and neat. When you have finished, put down your pencils and look at me.*

Have children answer questions 1 through 3 and stop on page 2.

Reading Comprehension; Vocabulary Strategies; Literary Elements; Text Features and Study Skills; Grammar, Mechanics, and Usage,
pages 3–17

Have children turn to page 3. Say: *You will now read some selections and answer some multiple-choice and short-answer questions. We will work through the text together. Read each selection carefully. Then we will read the questions that follow it. For each multiple-choice question, listen carefully as I read each answer choice. You will see that the lines in some selections are numbered. These numbers will help you find the lines or sentences you will need to answer the questions.*

After I read the answer choices, fill in the oval next to the answer you have chosen. Mark only one oval for each question. Mark your answers very carefully and make your marks dark and neat.

Stop when you reach the stop sign and wait for me to tell you to go on. When you have finished, put down your pencils and look at me. You may begin now.

Have children answer questions 4–20 and stop on page 17.

Phonemic Awareness/Phonics; Structural Analysis,
pages 18–20

Have children turn to page 18. Say: I *will now read you some questions. Listen very carefully. Then fill in the oval next to the best answer.*

Say: Look at Number 21. I will say the sounds in a word: /r/ /ō/ /b/. What word do you make when you blend these sounds together? Listen to these answer choices: rope, globe, robe. *Which answer choice represents the word you get when you blend the sounds /r/ /ō/ /b/.*

Say: Look at Number 22. I will say the sounds in a word: /l/ /ē/ /f/. What word do you make when you blend these sounds together? Listen to these answer choices: leaf, leash, reef. *Fill in the oval next to the picture that has the same sounds as /l/ /ē/ /f/*

Say: Look at Number 23. I will say a word: nail. *Now, listen to this sound /s/. What word do you have if you add the sound /s/ to the beginning of* nail? *Listen to these answer choices:* snail, sail, nail. *Fill in the oval next to the picture that represents the word you make when you add the sound /s/ to the beginning of the word* nail.

Say: I will say the name of each picture. After I say the name, read the three answer choices. Fill in the oval next to the word that names the picture. Look at number 24. I will say the name of the picture now. "Feet." "Feet." *Read the three answer choices and mark the answer next to the word* feet.

Continue in the same way through page 19.

Number 25: goat; Number 26: pail; Number 27: seal; Number 28: clay.

For Numbers 29 and 30, Have children turn to page 20. Say: *Listen carefully while I read each question and all three answer choices for each question. Then fill in the oval next to the answer you have chosen. Mark only one oval for each question. Mark your answers very carefully and make your marks dark and neat. When you have finished, put down your pencils and look at me.*

Writing,
pages 21–23

Have children turn to pages 21-23. Say: *Look a the writing prompt on page 21. It is followed by a planning page on page 22. Use this planning page to plan your composition. You may want to make notes or make a web to help put ideas in order. You may want to write a rough draft. The more planning you do, the clearer your composition will be.*

Have children turn to page 23. Say: *When you are ready to write your composition, be sure to write on the answer document on page 23, which is the page with lines. Your composition does not have to completely fill this lined page, but it must not be longer than the page.*

Student Name _____

Date _____

Unit
Assessment

TESTED SKILLS AND STRATEGIES

- Listening Comprehension
- Reading Comprehension
- Vocabulary Strategies
- Literary Elements
- Text Features and Study Skills
- Grammar, Mechanics, and Usage
- Phonemic Awareness/Phonics
- Structural Analysis
- Writing

Macmillan/McGraw-Hill

DIRECTIONS
Listen as your teacher reads the selection. Then answer each question.

1 How does Charlie solve his problem?

  (A) He makes ants on a log.

  (B) He makes cupcakes.

  (C) His sister makes something for him.

2 Why is Charlie upset at the beginning?

  (A) Because he had a bad day at school

  (B) Because his sister had too much homework

  (C) Because he doesn't have anything for the bake sale

3 Charlie couldn't wait any —

  (A) longer

  (B) longest

  (C) long

STOP

© Macmillan/McGraw-Hill

DIRECTIONS
Read the selection. Then answer each question.

My New Dog

I wanted a pet dog. My mom and dad said that I could have one. We went to the pet shelter. They have stray dogs who need a home. We saw many nice dogs! They were all pretty and cute. It was hard to pick one.

Page 3

GO ON

A woman showed us a puppy. She told me that he is very nice and likes to play. She let me carry the puppy. He licked my hand and gave a little yip. He wagged his tail and looked very happy.

Page 4

The puppy was so small and so soft. I <u>wanted</u> to take him home. My mom and dad said I could. We called him Joe.

Page 5

After we got home, my dad showed me how to feed him. Having a pet is a lot of work. You need to give dogs meals and water, but you should not <u>overfeed</u>. Then my dad told me that Joe needed to run and play outside. That will help him grow big.

© Macmillan/McGraw-Hill

Page 6

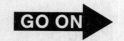

Unit Assessment

A dog should be walked every day. I use a long leash to walk Joe. Joe likes to play ball, too. I could not wait to <u>show</u> Joe to my friends!

Page 7

4 Read the chart.

Retell
The girl goes to the shelter.
The girl meets a puppy.
The girl takes a puppy home.

What goes on the last line of the chart?

(A) The puppy licks the girls hand.

(B) The girl names the puppy Joe.

(C) The girl takes the puppy for a walk.

5 What is the meaning of the word <u>show</u> on page 7?

(A) a performance

(B) to share

(C) to care

6 What did Joe do when he first met the girl?

  A He hid from her.

  B He licked her hand.

  C He ate his food.

7 The word <u>overfeed</u> on page 6 means —

  A feed too much

  B feed too little

  C feed the right amount

8 Why did the author write this story?

  A To tell about her new pet dog

  B To describe all kinds of dogs

  C To explain what pet shelters do

© Macmillan/McGraw-Hill

GO ON

9 On page 5, the word <u>wanted</u> means —

    (A) used to want

    (B) still wants

    (C) wants tommorow

10 Read this dictionary entry.

    little: not strong or loud.

Which sentence uses the same meaning of <u>little</u>?

    (A) Joe gave a little yip.

    (B) Stay here for a little while.

    (C) The pillow did little to help.

11 What happened after the girl brought Joe home?

_____

_____

_____

_____

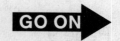

Page 10

DIRECTIONS
Read the poem. Then answer the question.

Diving

1 I'll jump off the board,
2 My arms out, I'll soar,
3 Down into the blue
4 Waters of the pool.

12 How many beats can you hear in each line?

(A) 5

(B) 3

(C) 7

STOP

DIRECTIONS
Answer each question.

13 Read Ruth's to-do list for her party.

What is the third thing Ruth will do?

(A) Bake a cake

(B) Put up decorations

(C) Invite friends

> ### To-Do List
> 1. Invite friends
> 2. Bake a cake
> 3. Put up decorations
> 4. Have a party

14 Look at the telephone directory.

What is Kelly Jones's phone number?

(A) 555-4217

(B) 575-9338

(C) 555-3232

James, Kenny --------------------	555-4217
Johnson, Kate -------------------	555-7759
Johnson, Mika ------------------	555-0257
Jones, Kelly ---------------------	555-3232
Jones, Rosa ---------------------	555-9338
Jones, Seth----------------------	555-1788

15 Look at the chart.

Where Animals Live		
Farm	**Woods**	**Water**
cow	deer	fish
chicken	bear	clam

What do bears and deer have in common?

A They live in water.

B They live with cows.

C They live in the woods.

16 Look at the picture.

Most hens lay one egg a day.

What does the caption tell about the picture?

A How hens lay eggs.

B Where hens lay eggs.

C How many eggs hens lay.

DIRECTIONS
This is a story that Tom wrote. The story has mistakes.
Read the story. Then answer the questions.

My Big Brother

(1) erik is my older brother. (2) He was born on April 24, 1999 (3) Sometimes he takes me to the movies.

GO ON ➡

17 What is the **BEST** way to write sentence 2?

(A) He was born on April 24, 1999.

(B) He, was born on April 24 1999.

(C) He was born, on April 24 1999.

18 Which sentence needs a capital letter?

(A) Sentence 1

(B) Sentence 2

(C) Sentence 3

GO ON

DIRECTIONS

This is a story that Jael wrote. The story has mistakes. Read the story. Then answer the questions.

Farm Life

(1) My family lives on a farm. (2) We has many hens and cows. (3) There is a lot of work on a farm. (4) Every morning I does my chores.

19 What is the **BEST** way to write sentence 2?

(A) We haves many hens and cows.

(B) We have many hens and cows.

(C) We having many hens and cows.

20 What is the **BEST** way to write sentence 4?

(A) Every morning I do my chores.

(B) Every morning I doing my chores.

(C) Every morning I done my chores.

STOP

Page 17

Listen while your teacher reads the directions.

21 (A)  (B)  (C)

22 (A)  (B)  (C)

23 (A) 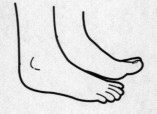 (B) (C)

Choose the word that names the picture.

24

    (A) fit

    (B) fat

    (C) feet

Page 18

GO ON

Student Name _____

25
(A) got
(B) gate
(C) goat

26
(A) pal
(B) pack
(C) pail

27
(A) sail
(B) seal
(C) slam

28
(A) clay
(B) class
(C) clap

GO ON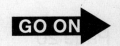

Unit Assessment   Grade 1 • Unit 4   **93**

Answer these questions.

29 Cats are _____than fish.

     (A) cute

     (B) cuter

     (C) cutest

30 Kate _____the final score.

     (A) tally

     (B) tallys

     (C) tallies

STOP

WRITTEN COMPOSITION

Write about a special book and tell why you think a friend should read it.

Think about the information in the box below when you write your composition.

REMEMBER TO –

- write about a special book and tell why a friend should read it

- make sure that every sentence you write helps the reader understand your composition

- include enough details to help the reader clearly understand what you are saying

- use correct spelling, capitalization, punctuation, grammar, and sentences

© Macmillan/McGraw-Hill

Page 21

USE THIS PREWRITING PAGE TO
PLAN YOUR COMPOSITION

MAKE SURE THAT YOU WRITE YOUR COMPOSITION ON
THE LINES ON PAGE 23

Unit Assessment

Answer Document

_____

_____

_____

_____

_____

_____

_____

_____

_____

Page 23

Student Name_____

Grade 1 • Unit 4
Student Evaluation Chart

Tested Skills	Number Correct	Percent Correct
Listening Comprehension: *Plot 1; Character, 2; Inflectional Endings, 3*	/3	%
Reading Comprehension: *Retell, 4; Main Idea and Details, 6; Author's Purpose, 8*	/3	%
Short answer: *Retell,* 11	/3	%
Vocabulary Strategies: *Multiple-Meaning Words, 5; Compound Words, 7; Inflected Endings, 9; Use a Dictionary, 10*	/4	%
Literary Elements: *Rhythm, 12*	/1	%
Text Features and Study Skills: *Numbered List, 13; Telephone Directory, 14; Chart, 15; Captions, 16*	/4	%
Grammar, Mechanics, and Usage: *Commas, 17; Capitalization, 18; Present-Tense Verbs, 19, 20*	/4	%
Phonemic Awareness: *Phoneme Blending, 21, 22; Phoneme Addition, 23*	/3	%
Phonics: *long e, 24, 27; long o, 25; long a, 26, 28*	/5	%
Structural Analysis: *Inflectional Endings, 29, 30*	/2	%
Writing: *Expository: Persuasive Report*	/4	%
Total Unit Test Score	/36	%

Unit Assessment

Grade 1 • Unit 5

This Unit Assessment is designed to measure your children's mastery of the skills taught in the unit. The test assesses all of the following areas:

- Listening Comprehension
- Reading Comprehension
- Vocabulary Strategies
- Literary Elements
- Text Features and Study Skills
- Grammar, Mechanics, and Usage
- Phonemic Awareness/Phonics
- Structural Analysis
- Writing

Listening Comprehension, page 2

Say: *Listen while I read this story to you. You will be asked to answer three multiple-choice questions based on this story. Listen carefully. We will begin now.*

How Plants Grow

Like all living things, plants grow in stages. The first stage begins with a little seed. Most seeds grow in the ground. The seed soaks up water and food from the dirt. It starts to grow roots and a shoot. The roots grow down into the wet ground. The shoot grows up toward the warmer sunlight and air.

In the second stage the shoot breaks through the ground and grows leaves. The plant is now a seedling. The seedling grows above ground and below ground. Above ground the seedling grows taller and bigger. Underground, the roots grow longer and deeper into the soil.

In the third stage the plant is grown. It makes a flower. The flower makes pollen. The pollen from the flower is taken to the other flowers. The pollen from the plant will help other plants make new seeds. The seeds the plant helped to make will grow into new plants.

Now have children turn to page 2. Read the directions at the top of the page. Then say: *Listen carefully while I read each question. Listen to all three answer choices for each question. Then fill in the oval next to the answer you have chosen. Mark only one oval for each question. Mark your answers very carefully and make your marks dark and neat. When you have finished, put down your pencils and look at me.*

Have children answer questions 1 through 3 and stop on page 2.

Reading Comprehension; Vocabulary Strategies; Literary Elements; Text Features and Study Skills; Grammar, Mechanics, and Usage, pages 3–17

Have children turn to page 3. Say: *You will now read some selections and answer some multiple-choice and short-answer questions. We will work though the test together. Read each selection carefully. Then we will read the questions that follow it. For each multiple-choice question, listen carefully as I read each answer choice. You will see that the lines in some selections are numbered. These numbers will help you find the lines or sentences you will need to answer the questions.*

After I read the answer choices, fill in the oval next to the answer you have chosen. Mark only one oval for each question. Mark your answers very carefully and make your marks dark and neat. Stop when you reach the stop sign and wait for me to tell you to go on. When you have finished, put down your pencils and look at me. You may begin now.

Have children answer questions 4–18 and stop on page 17.

Phonemic Awareness/Phonics; Structural Analysis,
pages 18–20

Have children turn to page 18. Say: *I will now read you some questions. Listen very carefully. Then fill in the oval next to the best answer. Look at Number 21. I will say the sounds in a word: /b/ /ō/ /t/. What word do you make when you blend these sounds together? Listen to these answer choices:* coat, boat, bone. *Which answer choice represents the word you get when you blend the sounds /b/ /ō/ /t/.*

Say: *Look at Number 22. I will say the sounds in a word: /b/ /ir/ /d/. What word do you make when you blend these sounds together? Listen to these answer choices:* barn, girl, bird. *Fill in the circle next to the picture that has the same sounds as /b/ /ir/ /d/.*

Say: *Look at Number 23. I will say a word:* corn */k/ /or/ /n/. What is the middle sound in* corn?. *Listen to these answer choices:* fork, star, wolf. *Fill in the circle next to the picture that has the same middle sound as* corn.

Say: *I will say the name of each picture. After I say the name, read the three answer choices. Fill in the oval next to the word that names the picture. Look at Number 24. I will say the name of the picture now. "Clown." "Clown." Read the three answer choices and mark the answer next to the word "Clown."*

Continue in the same way through page 20.

Number 25: horn; Number 26: cloud; Number 27: arm; Number 28: coin.

For Numbers 29 and 30, Have students turn to page 20. Say: *Listen carefully while I read each question and all three answer choices for each question. Then fill in the oval next to the answer you have chosen. Mark only one oval for each question. Make your answers very carefully and make your marks dark and neat. When you have finished, put down your pencils and look at me.*

Writing,
pages 21–23

Have children turn to pages 21–23. Say: *Look at the writing prompt on page 21. It is followed by planning page 22. Use this blank page to plan your composition. You may want to make notes or make a web to help put ideas in order. You may want to write a rough draft. The more planning you do, the clearer your composition will be.*

Have children turn to page 23. Say: *When you are ready to write your composition, be sure to write on the answer document on page 23, which is the page with lines. Your composition does not have to completely fill this lined page, but it must not be longer than the page.*

Student Name _____

Date _____

Unit Assessment

TESTED SKILLS AND STRATEGIES

- **Listening Comprehension**
- **Reading Comprehension**
- **Vocabulary Strategies**
- **Literary Elements**
- **Text Features and Study Skills**
- **Grammar, Mechanics, and Usage**
- **Phonemic Awareness/Phonics**
- **Structural Analysis**
- **Writing**

Macmillan/McGraw-Hill

Student Name _____

DIRECTIONS
Listen as your teacher reads the selection. Then answer each question.

1 The ways that roots and shoots grow are different because —

    A roots grow down and shoots grow up

    B roots and shoots both grow down

    C roots make a flower and shoots make pollen

2 What is the first stage of plant growth?

    A The shoot breaks through the ground.

    B The seed grows in the ground.

    C The flower makes pollen.

3 The shoot grows up toward the —

    A warms sunlight

    B warmer sunlight

    C warmiest sunlight

STOP

The Little Fish

A long time ago, a little fish lived in a little lake. The fish seemed very happy. It swam. It ate. It played. The little fish lived a very good life. It even had many animal friends.

GO ON ➡

Page 3

One day a duck stopped to see its friend the fish.

"Good day, fish," said the duck. "How are you?"

"Very well, thank you," said the fish. "You were away for a very long time. Did you go very <u>far</u> away?"

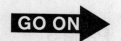

Unit Assessment

"I flew," said the duck. "I went to a big lake nearby and saw a little fish. The fish was just like you!"

The duck told the fish about all the things he saw on his travels.

GO ON

© Macmillan/McGraw-Hill

After the duck went away, the fish was very sad.
Suddenly it did not like swimming in the lake all alone.

"I want a friend to swim with me," the fish thought.
"I do not want to be alone." This thought made the
little fish so sad that it began to cry.

GO ON

Unit Assessment

The more the fish cried, the higher the water rose in the lake. Then the lake became too full. Some of the water began to spill over the side of the lake. It made a path to the other lake, forming a river.

The very next day, the two little fish saw each other. And now they are the very best of friends.

4 Read the chart.

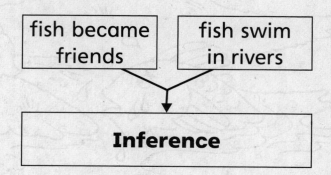

What goes in the Inference box?

(A) The fish swam in the river to meet one another.

(B) The lake was too full and the fish was crying.

(C) The fish cried and made a river.

5 Which word means the opposite of <u>far</u> on page 4?

(A) near

(B) before

(C) under

GO ON ➡

6 What happened after the duck went away?

(A) The fish was very happy.

(B) The fish was very unhappy.

(C) The fish played with its friends.

7 The duck saw that the fish was —

(A) swim

(B) swims

(C) swimming

8 Why did the lake overflow?

(A) The fish swam and played.

(B) The fish cried a lot.

(C) The fish was all alone.

GO ON

Page 9

9 The fish was so alone that it —

(A) cryed

(B) crid

(C) cried

10 Read this dictionary entry.

Fish: Noun. An animal that swims in water.

Which sentence uses the same meaning of fish?

(A) The fish swam in the river.

(B) I will fish for my dinner.

(C) The man will fish for clues.

11 What did the duck say that made the fish sad?

_____

_____

_____

_____

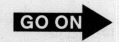

Unit Assessment

DIRECTIONS
Read the poem. Then answer the question.

Lovely Little Lauralie

1 Lovely Little Lauralie,

2 Loves her pony Penny.

3 She brought her six sweet sugar cubes,

4 But she didn't need that many.

5 Penny was already full

6 From eating all her hay, so—

7 Though Laura had six sugar cubes,

8 Penny would only say neigh.

---

12 Which line from the poem uses alliteration?

(A) Line 1

(B) Line 4

(C) Line 8

STOP

DIRECTIONS

Answer each question.

Use the picture and caption to answer questions 13 and 14.

Coach Gus helps Jenny and Mike learn baseball.

13 What is the name of the boy in the picture?

Ⓐ Mike

Ⓑ Jenny

Ⓒ Coach Gus

© Macmillan/McGraw-Hill

14 Who is helping the children learn baseball?

(A) Mike

(B) Jenny

(C) Coach Gus

15 Read the following sentences.

There are many kinds of **snakes.** They come in many different sizes. Some are poisonous, some are not.

The bold print tells you that the passage is mainly about —

(A) poison

(B) size

(C) snakes

16 Where in a book would you look to find the names of every chapter?

(A) Back cover

(B) Title page

(C) Table of contents

STOP

DIRECTIONS

This is a story that Ellie wrote. The story has mistakes.
Read the story. Then answer the questions.

The Firehouse

(1) On tuesday it rained all day. (2) My class walked
above the firehouse. (3) We saw a fire engine and talked
with Fred the Fireman.

© Macmillan/McGraw-Hill

17 What is the **BEST** way to write sentence 1?

(A) On Tuesday it rained all day.

(B) On tuesday It rained all day.

(C) On TuesDay it rained all day.

18 What is the **BEST** way to write sentence 2?

(A) My class walked of the firehouse.

(B) My class walked with the firehouse.

(C) My class walked to the firehouse.

GO ON ➡

Page 15

DIRECTIONS
This is a story that Jonah wrote. The story has mistakes.
Read the story. Then answer the questions.

A Bear's Life

(1) It is easy for bears to find food in the summer. (2) But in winter they cannot find food (3) Bears take very longest naps in winter.

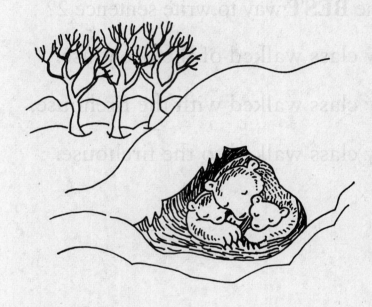

GO ON

19 What is the **BEST** way to write sentence 2?

(A) But in winter they cant find food.

(B) But in winter they can'nt find food.

(C) But in winter they can't find food.

20 What is the **BEST** way to write sentence 3?

(A) Bears take very long naps in winter.

(B) Bears take very longer naps in winter.

(C) Bears take very longed naps in winter.

STOP

© Macmillan/McGraw-Hill

Listen while your teacher reads the directions.

21 (A)    (B)    (C)

22 (A)    (B)    (C)

23 (A)    (B)    (C)

Choose the word that names the picture.

24    (A) clay

(B) clown

(C) clump

25

(A) horn

(B) hand

(C) thorny

26

(A) coin

(B) clam

(C) cloud

27

(A) aiming

(B) arm

(C) yarn

28

(A) corn

(B) coin

(C) gown

© Macmillan/McGraw-Hill

Page 19

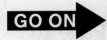

Answer these questions.

29 Dr. Stark is much —

(A) nice

(B) nicer

(C) nicest

30 If you lose your homework, you will have to —

(A) undo it

(B) redo it

(C) not do it

STOP

WRITTEN COMPOSITION

Write about how you get ready to go to school in the morning.

Think about the information in the box below when you write your composition.

> **REMEMBER TO –**
>
> - write about how you get ready to go to school in the morning
>
> - make sure that every sentence you write helps the reader understand your composition
>
> - include enough details to help the reader clearly understand what you are saying
>
> - use correct spelling, capitalization, punctuation, grammar, and sentences

© Macmillan/McGraw-Hill

Page 21

Student Name _____

MAKE SURE THAT YOU WRITE YOUR COMPOSITION ON
THE LINES ON PAGE 23

Unit Assessment

© Macmillan/McGraw-Hill

Student Name _____

Answer Document

_____

_____

_____

_____

_____

_____

_____

_____

_____

Page 23

Student Name _____

Grade 1 • Unit 5
Student Evaluation Chart

Tested Skills	Number Correct	Percent Correct
Listening Comprehension: *Compare and Contrast, 1; Sequence, 2; Inflectional Endings, 3*	/3	%
Reading Comprehension: *Make Inferences, 4; Sequence, 6; Cause and Effect, 8*	/3	%
Short answer: *Cause and Effect, 11*	/3	%
Vocabulary Strategies: *Antonyms, 5; Inflectional Endings, 7, 9; Use a Dictionary, 10*	/4	%
Literary Elements: *Alliteration, 12*	/1	%
Text Features and Study Skills: *Use Photographs and Captions, 13, 14; Bold Print, 15; Book Parts, 16*	/4	%
Grammar, Mechanics, and Usage: *Capitalize Proper Nouns, 17; Prepositions, 18; Contractions, 19; Adjectives, 20*	/4	%
Phonemic Awareness: *Phoneme Blending, 21, 22; Phoneme Isolation, 23*	/3	%
Phonics: *Diphthongs /ou/, 24, 26; r-Controlled Vowel or, 25; r-Controlled Vowel ar, 27; Diphthongs /oi/, 28*	/5	%
Structural Analysis: *Inflectional Endings, 29; Prefixes re- and un-, 30*	/2	%
Writing: *Expository: How-to*	/4	%
Total Unit Test Score	/36	%

© Macmillan/McGraw-Hill

This Unit Assessment is designed to measure your children's mastery of the skills taught in the unit. The test assesses all of the following areas:

- Listening Comprehension
- Reading Comprehension
- Vocabulary Strategies
- Literary Elements
- Text Features and Study Skills
- Grammar, Mechanics, and Usage
- Phonemic Awareness/Phonics
- Structural Analysis
- Writing

Listening Comprehension,
page 2

Say: *Listen while I read this story to you. You will be asked to answer three multiple-choice questions based on this story. Listen carefully. We will begin now.*

Bird Watching

You can learn a lot about birds just by watching them. Even in a huge city, you can watch birds finding food, building nests, and caring for their babies. What things have you watched birds do?

You will see some birds fly from tree to tree. Sparrows, robins, and cardinals like to rest on tree branches. Other birds like to peck at the ground most of the day. You will often see pigeons walking around on the ground when they look for food.

Some kinds of birds do things that no other birds do. A mockingbird learns how to sing the songs of many other birds. Some mockingbirds can sing over ten different bird songs! Woodpeckers use their beaks to pound holes in thick tree trunks. And hummingbirds flap their wings so fast that they can not be seen.

So the next time you want to learn some interesting facts about birds, just look outside of your windows. You can use a bird book to help you figure out which bird is which.

Now have children turn to page 2. Read the directions at the top of the page. Then say: *Listen carefully while I read each question. Listen to all three answer choices for each question. Then fill in the oval next to the answer you have chosen. Mark only one oval for each question. Mark your answers very carefully and make your marks dark and neat. When you have finished, put down your pencils and look at me.*

Have children answer questions 1 through 3 and stop on page 2.

Reading Comprehension; Vocabulary Strategies; Literary Elements; Text Features and Study Skills; Grammar, Mechanics, and Usage,
pages 3–17

Have children turn to page 3. Say: *You will now read some selections and answer some multiple-choice and short-answer questions. We will work though the test together. Read each selection carefully. Then we will read the questions that follow it. For each multiple-choice question, listen carefully as I read each answer choice. You will see that the lines in some selections are numbered. These numbers will help you find the lines or sentences you will need to answer the questions.*

After I read the answer choices, fill in the oval next to the answer you have chosen. Mark only one oval for each question. Mark your answers very carefully and make your marks dark and neat. Stop when you reach the stop sign and wait for me to tell you to go on. When you have finished, put down your pencils and look at me. You may begin now.

Have children answer questions 4–18 and stop on page 17.

Phonemic Awareness/Phonics; Structural Analysis,
pages 18–20

Have children turn to page 18. Say: I will now read you some questions. Listen very carefully. Then fill in the oval next to the best answer. Look at Number 21. I will say a word: good, /g/ /ù/ /d/. What is the middle sound in good? Listen to these answer choices: boot, book, spoon. Fill in the oval next to the picture that has the same middle sound as good.

Say: Look at Number 22. I will say a word: boil, /b/ /oi/ /l/. What is the middle sound in boil? Listen to these answer choices: coin, cow, moon. Fill in the oval next to the picture that has the same middle sound as boil.

Say: Look at Number 23. I will say the sounds in a word: claw /k/ /l/ /aw/. What word do you make if you blend these sounds together? Listen to these answer choices: clam, claw, clay. Fill in the oval next to the picture that shows the word that you make when you blend /k/ /l/ /aw/.

Say: I will say the name of each picture. After I say the name, read the three answer choices. Fill in the oval next to the word that names the picture. Look at Number 24. I will say the name of the picture now. "Hook." "Hook." Read the three answer choices and mark the answer next to the word "hook."

Continue in the same way through page 20. Number 25: saw; Number 26: moon.

For Numbers 27 and 28, read the questions and have children fill in the oval for the correct answer.

For Numbers 29 and 30, have children turn to page 20. Say: Listen carefully while I read each question and all three answer choices for each question, Then fill in the oval next to the answer you have chosen. Mark only one oval for each question. Mark your answers very carefully and make your marks dark and neat. When you have finished, put down your pencils and look at me.

Writing,
pages 21–23

Have children turn to pages 21–23. Say: Look at the writing prompt on page 21. It is followed by planning page 22. Use this blank page to plan your composition. You may want to make notes or make a web to help put ideas in order. You may want to write a rough draft. The more planning you do, the clearer your composition will be.

Have children turn to page 23. Say: When you are ready to write your composition, be sure to write on the answer document on page 23, which is the page with lines. Your composition does not have to completely fill this lined page, but it must not be longer than the page.

Student Name _____

Date _____

Unit
Assessment
TESTED SKILLS AND STRATEGIES

- **Listening Comprehension**
- **Reading Comprehension**
- **Vocabulary Strategies**
- **Literary Elements**
- **Text Features and Study Skills**
- **Grammar, Mechanics, and Usage**
- **Phonemic Awareness/Phonics**
- **Structural Analysis**
- **Writing**

Mc Graw Hill   Macmillan/McGraw-Hill

DIRECTIONS

Listen as your teacher reads the selection. Then answer each question.

1 What do sparrows, robins, and cardinals like to do?

    (A) Sing many different bird songs

    (B) Pound holes in trees

    (C) Rest on tree branches

2 Pigeons are a type of bird that —

    (A) pounds holes into trees

    (B) looks for food on the ground

    (C) sings the songs of many birds

3 The word <u>cannot</u> can be written as —

    (A) cann't

    (B) can't

    (C) cant

STOP

DIRECTIONS
Read the selection. Then answer each question.

Jim's Fun Picnic

Jim had a picnic in the summer. It was on a beautiful, sunny day.

Jim worked hard to plan his picnic. He wanted it to be the best picnic ever.

GO ON ▶

© Macmillan/McGraw-Hill

First, Jim thought about which people to <u>invite</u> to come to the picnic. He asked some friends and his family. Next, he picked a spot to have the picnic. He picked a spot with lots of space for people to eat and play. Some good spots for a picnic are in a park, next to a lake, in a forest, or at a beach.

Page 4

Unit Assessment

Everyone had fun at Jim's picnic. There was a lot of good food. They all ate sandwiches. They also ate some other foods. They ate watermelon, grapes, and corn on the cob. Jim's friends liked the food he picked. After lunch they played games.

Page 5

GO ON

Jim wanted to keep his picnic <u>safe</u>. He wore a helmet when he rode his bike. He had a first-aid kit for accidental cuts and scrapes. Jim cared about his friends.

Page 6

GO ON ➡

Jim played many games at his picnic. He played catch with his pals. The children had a fun water fight. Some of them even played hide-and-seek. Jim had lots of fun planning his picnic. He wanted to plan one again very soon.

4 Read the chart.

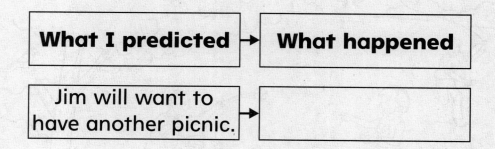

What goes in the "What happened" box?

(A) Jim wants to plan a picnic again soon.

(B) Jim does not want to plan another picnic.

(C) Jim is not sure he wants to plan a picnic.

5 The base word of <u>planning</u> is —

(A) plan

(B) plain

(C) plann

GO ON

Unit Assessment

6 This story is realistic because —

(A) all of the events could happen

(B) some of the events could happen

(C) none of the events could happen

7 Which word means the opposite of <u>safe</u> —

(A) easy

(B) hard

(C) dangerous

8 Which words help you to know the meaning of <u>invite</u> on page 4?

(A) to come to the picnic

(B) first Jim thought about

(C) Jim picked a spot

9 Jim brings a first-aid kit to —

    (A) invite his friends and family

    (B) play hide and seek

    (C) keep his friends safe

10 Read this dictionary entry.

    care: Verb. to help out.

Which sentence uses the same meaning of <u>care</u>?

    (A) Jim rode his bike with care.

    (B) Jim cared about the game.

    (C) Jim cared for his friends.

11 Describe how Jim planned his picnic.

_____

_____

_____

_____

DIRECTIONS
Read the poem. Then aswer the question.

Pass the Veggies

1   Carrots, celery, sweet snap peas,

2   Pass the veggies, quickly please.

3   I just want to eat them up.

4   Vegetable soup? Give me a cup.

5   I don't want butter and who needs cheese.

6   Just pass the veggies! Quickly please!

12 Which line could replace line 5?

   (A) Food from the earth and food from the field

   (B) Food from the earth and food from the trees

   (C) Food from the earth and food from the hill

Student Name_____

DIRECTIONS
Answer each question.

Use the article to answer questions 13 and 14.

HURRICANES

What Is a Hurricane?
A hurricane is a large storm. It brings strong winds and heavy rain.

Where Do Hurricanes Start?
Hurricanes start over the ocean.

How Strong Are Hurricanes?
Hurricanes can have very heavy winds that blow over 75 miles per hour.

---

13 In this article, you will find information on —

    A the strength of a hurricane

    B other types of storms

    C the strength of a tornado

14 What is another heading you might find in this article?

    A When do tornadoes occur?

    B When do hurricanes occur?

    C How loud is thunder?

Page 12

Student Name _____

15 Read this Web page.

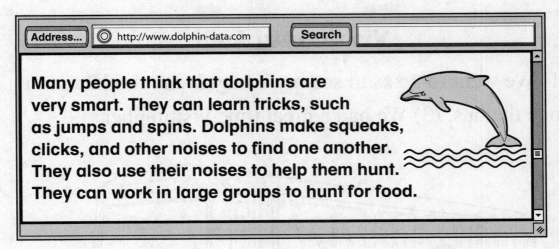

Address... ○ http://www.dolphin-data.com   Search [   ]

Many people think that dolphins are very smart. They can learn tricks, such as jumps and spins. Dolphins make squeaks, clicks, and other noises to find one another. They also use their noises to help them hunt. They can work in large groups to hunt for food.

The person who found this Web page might have searched for —

(A) dolphin sounds

(B) ocean currents

(C) killer whales

16 Look at the list. Which of these is something you would do before bed?

(A) Put on a backpack

(B) Wake up

(C) Wash your face

Getting ready for bed
—brush my teeth
—wash my face
—wash my hands
—put on my pajamas

STOP

This is a story that Lisa wrote. The story has mistakes.
Read the story. Then answer the questions.

Visiting My Aunt

(1) We went to texas to see my aunt. (2) my mother and i
rode the bus. (3) We had a great time visiting her.

© Macmillan/McGraw-Hill

17 What is the **BEST** way to write sentence 1?

    A We Went to texas to see my aunt.

    B We went to Texas to see my aunt.

    C We went to texas to see my Aunt

18 What is the **BEST** way to write sentence 2?

    A My mother and i rode the bus.

    B My mother and I rode the bus.

    C My Mother and I rode the bus.

GO ON

DIRECTIONS

This is a story that Ben wrote. The story has mistakes. Read the story. Then answer the questions.

A New Pet

(1) I have a new puppy at home (2) My puppy is named Sam. (3) Today Grandfather came for a visit. (4) Has him seen the new puppy?

© Macmillan/McGraw-Hill

19 What is the subject in sentence 3?

    Ⓐ visit

    Ⓑ came

    Ⓒ Grandfather

20 What is the **BEST** way to write sentence 4?

    Ⓐ Has he seen the new puppy?

    Ⓑ Has his seen the new puppy?

    Ⓒ Has she seen the new puppy?

STOP

Listen while your teacher reads the directions.

21 (A)    (B)    (C)

22 (A)    (B) 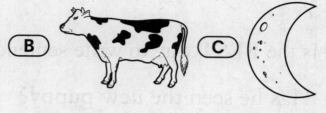   (C)

23 (A)    (B)    (C)

Choose the word that names the picture.

24

(A) hook

(B) book

(C) hoot

GO ON ▶

Unit Assessment

25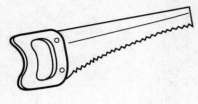

(A) sow

(B) saw

(C) sew

26

(A) mule

(B) moon

(C) men

27 Which word has a closed syllable?

(A) apple

(B) backpack

(C) baby

28 Which second syllable is correct?

(A) candal

(B) candle

(C) candul

Page 19

GO ON

Student Name ______________________________

Answer these questions.

29 Don't forget to bring —

(A) you backpack

(B) mine backpack

(C) your backpack

30 Another way to write will not is —

(A) willn't

(B) wont

(C) won't

WRITTEN COMPOSITION

Write a report on how to plan a picnic.

Think about the information in the box below when you write your report.

REMEMBER TO –

- write about how to plan a picnic

- make sure that every sentence you write helps the reader understand your composition

- include enough details to help the reader clearly understand what you are saying

- use correct spelling, capitalization, punctuation, grammar, and sentences

Page 21

USE THIS PREWRITING PAGE TO
PLAN YOUR COMPOSITION

MAKE SURE THAT YOU WRITE YOUR COMPOSITION ON
THE LINES ON PAGE 23

© Macmillan/McGraw-Hill

Unit Assessment

Answer Document

_____

_____

_____

_____

_____

_____

_____

_____

_____

Page 23

Student Name _____

Student Evaluation Chart

Tested Skills	Number Correct	Percent Correct
Listening Comprehension: *Classify and Categorize*, 1, 2; *Contractions*, 3	/3	%
Reading Comprehension: *Make and Confirm Predictions*, 4; *Fantasy and Reality*, 6; *Make Inferences*, 9	/3	%
Short answer: *Character*, 11	/3	%
Vocabulary Strategies: *Inflectional Endings*, 5; *Antonyms*, 7; *Context Clues*, 8; *Use a Dictionary*, 10	/4	%
Literary Elements: *Rhyming Patterns*, 12	/1	%
Text Features and Study Skills: *Headings*, 13, 14; *Media and Web Resources*, 15; *Lists*, 16	/4	%
Grammar, Mechanics, and Usage: *Capitalization*, 17, 18; *Subjects and Predicates*, 19; *Pronouns*, 20	/4	%
Phonemic Awareness: *Phoneme Isolation*, 21, 22; *Phoneme Blending*, 23	/3	%
Phonics: *Digraphs oo*, 24, 26; *Digraphs /ô/*, 25; *Closed Syllables*, 27; *Final Stable Syllables*, 28	/5	%
Structural Analysis: *Possessive Pronouns*, 29; *Contractions*, 30	/2	%
Writing: *Expository: Persuasive Report*	/4	%
Total Unit Test Score	/36	%

Student Name _____

UNIT ASSESSMENT

S-1 Ⓐ Ⓑ Ⓒ   S-2 Ⓐ Ⓑ Ⓒ

1 Ⓐ Ⓑ Ⓒ   11 Ⓐ Ⓑ Ⓒ   21 Ⓐ Ⓑ Ⓒ
2 Ⓐ Ⓑ Ⓒ   12 Ⓐ Ⓑ Ⓒ   22 Ⓐ Ⓑ Ⓒ
3 Ⓐ Ⓑ Ⓒ   13 Ⓐ Ⓑ Ⓒ   23 Ⓐ Ⓑ Ⓒ
4 Ⓐ Ⓑ Ⓒ   14 Ⓐ Ⓑ Ⓒ   24 Ⓐ Ⓑ Ⓒ
5 Ⓐ Ⓑ Ⓒ   15 Ⓐ Ⓑ Ⓒ   25 Ⓐ Ⓑ Ⓒ
6 Ⓐ Ⓑ Ⓒ   16 Ⓐ Ⓑ Ⓒ   26 Ⓐ Ⓑ Ⓒ
7 Ⓐ Ⓑ Ⓒ   17 Ⓐ Ⓑ Ⓒ   27 Ⓐ Ⓑ Ⓒ
8 Ⓐ Ⓑ Ⓒ   18 Ⓐ Ⓑ Ⓒ   28 Ⓐ Ⓑ Ⓒ
9 Write answer   19 Ⓐ Ⓑ Ⓒ   29 Ⓐ Ⓑ Ⓒ
10 Ⓐ Ⓑ Ⓒ   20 Ⓐ Ⓑ Ⓒ   30 Ⓐ Ⓑ Ⓒ

STOP

Student Name _____

STUDENT ANSWER SHEET

9 _____

Unit Assessment

Student Name _____

UNIT ASSESSMENT

S-1 ⒶⒷⒸ   S-2 ⒶⒷⒸ

1 ⒶⒷⒸ   11 Write answer   21 ⒶⒷⒸ
2 ⒶⒷⒸ   12 ⒶⒷⒸ   22 ⒶⒷⒸ
3 ⒶⒷⒸ   13 ⒶⒷⒸ   23 ⒶⒷⒸ
4 ⒶⒷⒸ   14 ⒶⒷⒸ   24 ⒶⒷⒸ
5 ⒶⒷⒸ   15 ⒶⒷⒸ   25 ⒶⒷⒸ
6 ⒶⒷⒸ   16 ⒶⒷⒸ   26 ⒶⒷⒸ
7 ⒶⒷⒸ   17 ⒶⒷⒸ   27 ⒶⒷⒸ
8 ⒶⒷⒸ   18 ⒶⒷⒸ   28 ⒶⒷⒸ
9 ⒶⒷⒸ   19 ⒶⒷⒸ   29 ⒶⒷⒸ
10 ⒶⒷⒸ   20 ⒶⒷⒸ   30 ⒶⒷⒸ

STOP

STUDENT ANSWER SHEET

11 _____

_____

_____

_____

Short-Answer Reading Rubric

Use the rubric below to score the short-answer items in the tests.

Score	Description
3	An exemplary response gives an interesting and detailed response strongly supported by text evidence.
2	A sufficient response gives a clear and reasonable response supported by text evidence.
1	A partially sufficient response gives a reasonable but vague response weakly connected to text evidence.
0	An insufficient response does not respond to the question.

Evidence may be specific words from the story or a retelling.

Grade 1 Answer Key

Sample Questions

Question	Answer	Content Focus
S-1	B	Plot
S-2	A	Sentence Capitalization

UNIT 1

Question	Answer	Content Focus
1	C	Author's Purpose
2	C	Sequence
3	B	Double Final Consonants
4	A	Character
5	C	High-Frequency Words
6	B	Plot
7	A	High-Frequency Words
8	B	Sequence
9	See sample answers	Character
10	C	Rhyme
11	A	Photographs
12	C	Labels

Unit Assessment

Question	Answer	Content Focus
13	C	Lists
14	B	Parts of a Book
15	B	Sentences
16	C	Word Order
17	A	Capitalization
18	B	Punctuation
19	C	Phoneme Blending
20	A	Identify Rhyme
21	A	Phoneme Isolation
22	B	Short *a*
23	B	Short *a*
24	A	Short *i*
25	C	Consonant Blends
26	B	Consonant Blends
27	A	Consonant Blends
28	C	Inflectional Endings
29	B	Inflectional Endings
30	B	Double Final Consonants

Sample Answers for Question 9:

3-point answer: Flip can jump. He can tag the children. He can dig very fast. Flip can play with the children.

2-point answer: Flip can jump, tag, dig, and play.

1-point answer: Jump, tag, dig, play.

UNIT 2

Question	Answer	Content Focus
1	B	Sequence
2	C	Plot
3	B	Inflectional Endings
4	A	Main Idea and Details
5	C	High-Frequency Words
6	A	Main Idea and Details
7	B	High-Frequency Words
8	C	Main Idea and Details
9	See sample answers	Main Idea and Details
10	C	Rhythm
11	C	Diagrams
12	B	Dictionary
13	B	Follow Directions
14	C	Use Photographs
15	A	Proper Nouns
16	C	Plural Nouns
17	B	Plural Nouns
18	A	Plural Nouns
19	B	Phoneme Isolation
20	A	Phoneme Blending
21	C	Phoneme Blending

Question	Answer	Content Focus
22	C	Short *o*
23	C	Short *e*
24	C	Short *u*
25	B	Consonant Digraphs
26	A	Consonant Blends
27	A	Consonant Blends
28	B	Contractions
29	C	Inflectional Endings
30	B	Contractions

Sample Answers for Question 9:

3-point answer: In the story dogs learn many tricks. The story talks about dogs that can jump, fetch, and sit and come. A dog sits up when she wants to eat and another one jumps over bricks.

2-point answer: The story tells about dogs that can jump, fetch, come, sit up, and jump over bricks.

1-point answer: Jump, fetch, come, sit up, and jump over bricks.

UNIT 3

Question	Answer	Content Focus
1	C	Main Idea and Details
2	B	Compare and Contrast
3	A	Inflectional Endings
4	A	Make and Confirm Predictions
5	B	High-Frequency Words
6	B	Character
7	C	High-Frequency Words
8	A	Sequence
9	See sample answers	Plot
10	A	Sensory Language
11	B	Floor Plan
12	A	Newspapers and Periodicals
13	A	Chart
14	B	Signs and Symbols
15	B	Present-Tense Verbs
16	C	Present-Tense Verbs
17	B	Present-Tense Verbs
18	C	Past-Tense Verbs
19	C	Phoneme Deletion

Question	Answer	Content Focus
20	B	Phoneme Blending
21	A	Phoneme Isolation
22	B	Long *a*
23	B	Long *i*
24	B	Three-Letter Blends
25	A	Consonant Digraphs
26	B	Consonant Digraphs
27	A	Three-Letter Blends
28	C	Inflectional Endings
29	C	Inflectional Endings
30	A	Inflectional Endings

Sample Answers for Question 9:

3-point answer: Spike's problem is that he wants the children to play with him. He yips and yaps at them, but they do not notice him. Spike is not having fun at Jake's party. Finally, Spike gets some cake to eat.

2-point answer: Spike's problem is that the children will not play with him. He yips and yaps but they do not hear him or see him.

1-point answer: He wants to play.

UNIT 4

Question	Answer	Content Focus
1	A	Plot
2	C	Character
3	A	Inflectional Endings
4	C	Retell
5	B	Multiple-Meaning Words
6	B	Main Idea and Details
7	A	Compound Words
8	A	Author's Purpose
9	A	Inflectional Endings
10	A	Use a Dictionary
11	See sample answers	Retell
12	A	Rhythm
13	B	Numbered List
14	C	Telephone Directory
15	C	Chart
16	C	Captions
17	A	Commas
18	A	Capitalization
19	B	Present-Tense Verbs

Question	Answer	Content Focus
20	A	Present-Tense Verbs
21	C	Phoneme Blending
22	A	Phoneme Blending
23	C	Phoneme Addition
24	C	Long *e*
25	C	Long *o*
26	C	Long *a*
27	B	Long *e*
28	A	Long *a*
29	B	Inflectional Endings
30	C	Inflectional Endings

Sample Answers for Question 11:

3-point answer: After the girl brought the puppy home, her father showed her how to feed him. Then she took Joe for a walk. She put a long leash on Joe.

2-point answer: The girl fed Joe and then took him for a walk.

1-point answer: She took the dog for a walk.

UNIT 5

Question	Answer	Content Focus
1	A	Compare and Contrast
2	B	Sequence
3	B	Inflectional Endings
4	A	Make Inferences
5	A	Antonyms
6	B	Sequence
7	C	Inflectional Endings
8	B	Cause and Effect
9	C	Inflectional Endings
10	A	Use a Dictionary
11	See sample answers	Cause and Effect
12	A	Alliteration
13	A	Captions
14	C	Captions
15	C	Bold Print
16	C	Book Parts
17	A	Capitalization
18	C	Prepositions
19	C	Contractions
20	A	Adjectives

Question	Answer	Content Focus
21	B	Blending
22	C	Blending
23	A	Isolation
24	B	Diphthongs /ou/
25	A	*r*-controlled vowel *or*
26	C	Diphthongs /ou/
27	B	*r*-controlled vowel *ar*
28	B	Diphthongs /oi/
29	B	Inflectional Endings
30	B	Prefixes

Sample Answers for Question 11:

3-point answer: The duck told the fish that he was visiting another lake and met another fish. This made the fish upset because he realized for the first time that he was the only fish in his small lake and he was lonely.

2-point answer: The duck said that he was visiting another lake. He told the little fish that he met another small fish. This made the fish sad.

1-point answer: The duck made the fish sad.

UNIT 6

Question	Answer	Content Focus
1	C	Classify and Categorize
2	B	Classify and Categorize
3	B	Contractions
4	A	Make and Confirm Predictions
5	A	Inflectional Endings
6	A	Fantasy vs. Reality
7	C	Antonyms
8	A	Context Clues
9	C	Make Inferences
10	C	Use a Dictionary
11	See sample answers	Character
12	B	Rhyming Patterns
13	A	Headings
14	B	Headings
15	A	Media and Web Resources
16	C	List
17	B	Capitalization
18	B	Capitalization

Question	Answer	Content Focus
19	C	Subjects and Predicates
20	A	Pronouns
21	B	Phoneme Isolation
22	A	Phoneme Isolation
23	B	Phoneme Blending
24	A	Vowel Digraphs
25	B	Vowel Digraphs
26	B	Vowel Digraphs
27	B	Closed Syllables
28	B	Final Stable Syllables
29	C	Pronouns
30	C	Contractions

Sample Answers for Question 11:

3-point answer: Jim planned his picnic carefully. He thought about which people to invite to his picnic and invited both friends and family. He chose a spot for the picnic that he thought everyone would like. He planned special food and games for his picnic. He made sure they were healthy and brought a first-aid kit in case they got hurt.

2-point answer: Jim planned lots of things for his picnic. He planned who would come and where they would go. He planned what they would eat and what they would do. He played games with his guests and took care of them.

1-point answer: Jim planned food and games for his picnic. Everyone had fun.

WRITING RUBRICS
SCORE POINT 1

EACH COMPOSITION AT THIS SCORE POINT IS AN INEFFECTIVE PRESENTATION OF THE WRITER'S IDEAS.

Focus and Coherence
- Individual paragraphs and/or the entire composition are not focused. The writer may shift abruptly from idea to idea, making it difficult for the reader to understand how the ideas in the composition are related.
- The entire composition has little sense of completeness. The introduction and conclusion, if present, may be perfunctory.
- A large amount of writing may be unrelated and may not contribute to the development or quality of the entire composition. At times, the composition may be only weakly connected to the prompt.

Organization
- The writer's progression of thought between sentences and/or paragraphs is not logical. Occasionally weak progression results from a lack of transitions or from the use of transitions that do not make sense. At other times, the progression of thought is not evident, even if appropriate transitions are present.
- An organizational strategy is not evident. The writer may present ideas randomly, making the composition difficult to follow.
- Wordiness and/or repetition may inhibit the progression of ideas.

Development of Ideas
- The writer presents one or more ideas but provides little development of those ideas.
- The writer presents one or more ideas and makes an attempt to develop them. However, the development is general or vague, making it difficult for the reader to understand the writer's ideas.
- The writer presents only a plot summary of a published piece of writing, movie, or television show.
- The writer leaves out important information, which creates gaps between ideas. These gaps inhibit the reader's understanding of the ideas.

Voice
- The writer does not use language that engages the reader and therefore fails to establish a connection.
- There may be no evidence of the writer's individual voice. The composition does not sound authentic or original. The writer does not express his/her individuality or unique perspective.

Conventions
- There is little evidence in the composition that the writer can correctly apply the English language conventions. Severe and/or frequent errors in spelling, capitalization, punctuation, grammar, usage, and sentence structure may cause the writing to be difficult to read. These errors weaken the composition by causing a lack of fluency.
- The writer may misuse or omit words and phrases, and may frequently include awkward sentences. These weaknesses inhibit the effective communication of ideas.

SCORE POINT 2

EACH COMPOSITION AT THIS SCORE POINT IS A SOMEWHAT EFFECTIVE PRESENTATION OF THE WRITER'S IDEAS.

Focus and Coherence

- Individual paragraphs and/or the entire composition are somewhat focused. The writer may shift quickly from idea to idea, but the reader can easily understand how the ideas in the composition are related.

- The entire composition has some sense of completeness. The writer includes an introduction and conclusion, but they may be superficial.

- Some of the writing may be unrelated and may not contribute to the development or quality of the entire composition.

Organization

- The writer's progression of thought between sentences and/or paragraphs may not always be smooth or logical. Occasionally, the writer should strengthen the progression by including more meaningful transitions; at other times the writer needs to establish stronger links between ideas.

- The organizational strategies the writer chooses do not allow the writer to present ideas effectively.

- Some wordiness and/or repetition may be present, but these weaknesses do not completely inhibit the progression of ideas.

Development of Ideas

- The writer attempts to develop the composition by listing or briefly explaining the ideas. The development remains superficial, preventing the reader's full understanding of the writer's ideas.

- The writer presents one or more ideas and attempts to develop them. There is little evidence of depth of thinking. The development may be mostly general, inconsistent, or contrived.

- The writer may leave out small pieces of information that create minor gaps between ideas. These gaps do not inhibit the reader's understanding of the ideas.

Voice

- There may be moments when the writer uses language that engages the reader, but the writer fails to sustain the connection.

- Individual paragraphs or sections of the composition sound authentic or original, but the writer does not generally express his/her individuality or unique perspective.

Conventions

- Errors in spelling, capitalization, punctuation, grammar, usage, and sentence structure throughout the composition may indicate a limited control of English language conventions. These errors may not cause the writing to be unclear, however they may weaken the overall fluency of the composition.

- The writer may employ simple or inaccurate words and phrases, and may write some awkward sentences. These weaknesses inhibit the overall effectiveness of the communication of ideas.

SCORE POINT 3

EACH COMPOSITION AT THIS SCORE POINT IS A GENERALLY EFFECTIVE PRESENTATION OF THE WRITER'S IDEAS.

Focus and Coherence
- Individual paragraphs and the composition are, for the most part, focused. The writer generally shows the distinct relationship between ideas, rarely making sudden shifts from one idea to the next.
- The composition has a sense of completeness. The introduction and conclusion add depth to the composition.
- Most of the writing contributes to the development or quality of the entire composition.

Organization
- The writer's progression of thought between sentences and/or paragraphs is, for the most part, smooth and controlled. Usually, transitions are meaningful, and the links between ideas are logical.
- The organizational strategies the writer chooses are usually effective.
- Wordiness and repetition, if present, are minor problems that do not inhibit the progression of ideas.

Development of Ideas
- The writer attempts to develop all the ideas in the composition. Some ideas may be developed more thoroughly and specifically than others, but the development reflects some depth of thought, allowing the reader to generally understand and appreciate the writer's ideas.
- The writer's presentation of some ideas may be thoughtful. Little evidence exists that the writer has been willing to take compositional risks when developing the topic.

Voice
- The writer uses language that engages the reader and sustains that connection throughout most of the composition.
- In general, the composition sounds authentic and original. The writer usually expresses his/her individuality or unique perspective.

Conventions
- There is evidence that the writer generally demonstrates a good command of spelling, capitalization, punctuation, grammar, usage, and sentence structure. Although there may be minor errors, they create few disruptions in the fluency of the composition.
- The words, phrases, and sentence structures the writer employs are generally appropriate and contribute to the overall effectiveness of the communication of ideas.

SCORE POINT 4

EACH COMPOSITION AT THIS SCORE POINT IS A HIGHLY EFFECTIVE PRESENTATION OF THE WRITER'S IDEAS.

Focus and Coherence

- Individual paragraphs and the entire composition are focused. This sustained focus allows the reader to understand how the ideas included in the composition are related.
- The entire composition has a sense of completeness. The introduction and conclusion add meaningful depth to the composition.
- Most, if not all, of the writing contributes to the development or quality of the entire composition.

Organization

- The writer's progression of thought between sentences and/or paragraphs is smooth and controlled. The writer's use of meaningful transitions and the logical movement from idea to idea strengthen this progression.
- The organizational strategies the writer chooses allow the writer to present ideas clearly and effectively.

Development of Ideas

- The writer's thorough and specific development of each idea creates depth of thought in the composition, allowing the reader to fully understand and appreciate the writer's ideas.
- The writer's presentation of ideas is thoughtful or insightful. The writer may approach the topic from an unusual perspective, use his/her unique experiences or view of the world as a basis for writing, or make interesting connections between ideas. In all these cases, the writer's willingness to take compositional risks improves the quality of the composition.

Voice

- The writer uses language that engages the reader and sustains this connection throughout the composition.
- The composition sounds authentic and original. The writer expresses his/her individuality or unique perspective.

Conventions

- The strength of the conventions contributes to the effectiveness of the composition. The writer demonstrates a consistent command of spelling, capitalization, punctuation, grammar, usage, and sentence structure. When the writer communicates complex ideas through advanced forms of expression, he/she may make minor errors as a result of these compositional risks. These types of errors do not take away from the overall fluency of the composition.
- The words, phrases, and sentence structures the writer uses enhance the effectiveness of the communication of ideas.

Anchor Papers: Student Writing Samples

This section provides sample written responses to the Unit Assessment writing prompts, along with comments explaining the scores.

Unit 4: Expository: Persuasive Book Report

Score Point 1

My Spechul Book

Book is abowt lake wich is in the contry. It is called <u>Blue lake</u>. The sun and sand so sparkely. Mi dad lerns me to swim undr watr. I cud see fishes undr cleer watr If you read it its fun mabee we cud talk abowt it.

Focus and Coherence—Although the writer mentions a book, he or she does not give information to persuade the reader to read the book; instead, the writing expands on the topic of lakes and swimming.

Organization—The writer does not use the details to support a main idea.

Development of Ideas/Word Choice—The writing provides little or no development of ideas; omits or fails to use chosen words correctly (e.g., "Mi dad lerns me to swim undr watr").

Voice—The writer does not express a personal voice.

Conventions/Sentence Fluency—Makes frequent errors in grammar, spelling, mechanics, and usage; sentences run together or are confusing.

A Good Book

Last summer in July I read Good Times a special book to me. Its about a girl. Sandy. Its in a plase is hot and sunny. I like hot plases. Lots of things happen to her. I like Sandy and its good to read about her. She has a dog and they solve crimes. The ending is a suprise. You will like it too.

Focus and Coherence—The writer gives information about a book, but strays from the focus (e.g. " I like hot plases").

Organization—The writer omits a main idea or offers few or generic supporting details.

Development of Ideas/Word Choice—Attempts to develop ideas, but may be inconsistent; chooses words that are often ill-suited for the purpose, such as "its good to read about her."

Voice—The writer has difficulty expressing an inviting, unique tone.

Conventions/Sentence Fluency—Makes mistakes that can interfere with the reading of the writing; sentences flow in a somewhat fluid manner.

Score Point 3

The State Fair

The State Fair is a great book. The boy in the book is in a state fair. He is showing his pig. The pig's name is Charlie. Just as the winner is going to be told, somethin exsiting happens! If you read it, you can find out wat happens. Its a good book for families and friends to share.

Focus and Coherence—The writer gives information about a central topic and the focus is on persuading the reader.

Organization—Presents a main idea and supports it with details; the writing includes a topic sentence.

Development of Ideas/Word Choice—Attempts to develop ideas; uses word choice to suit the purpose; the writer employs persuasive language.

Voice—The writer uses a personal voice that generally expresses an inviting, unique tone.

Conventions/Sentence Fluency—Spelling, capitalization, punctuation, and usage are mostly correct; sentences lead naturally to those that follow.

Going to the Island

Going to the Island is about a pirate. His name is Captain Eddy. He has a parrit that talks. Captain Eddy takes lots of tresures. He has lots of fun. He gets in truble. In this story, he is a prisner. He has to get away. His parrit, Sam, helps him. You will like this story too. I want to read all of the Captain Eddy stories. You will too.

Focus and Coherence—The writer gives interesting and detailed information about a book; the focus of the report is clearly to persuade the reader to read a book.

Organization—Presents a main idea that is supported by clear, factual details; the ideas are presented in logical order.

Development of Ideas/Word Choice—Thoroughly develops ideas; uses precise word choice to enhance quality of content; the writer uses appropriately persuasive language (e.g. "You will like this story too").

Voice—The writer uses a personal voice that adds an inviting, unique tone to the writing.

Conventions/Sentence Fluency—Writing is almost entirely free of mechanical, grammatical, and spelling errors; sentences flow from one to the other.

Score Point 1

Getin ready for School

On school days im tired mostly. Not on saterday or sunday tho. After my sister wake me we eat serel with milk, my dog liks milk to. I can dres mysef and I get my book bag. The skoolbus to pik us up most days. We may b getting a car nest yeer tho?

Focus and Coherence—Does not give information about a central topic; the writer does not focus on a single topic, but instead jumps between several topics; this piece is not coherent.

Organization—Because the writing is not focused on a single topic, there is not a single main idea, and there are few coherent details.

Development of Ideas/Word Choice—Provides little or no development of ideas; the writer does not focus or develop any concept; omits or fails to use chosen words correctly; the writer has failed to write coherently; "The skoolbus to pick us up most days."; in this sentence, the writer has failed to use the correct verb forms and the sentence does not makes sense.

Voice—The writer does not express a personal voice.

Conventions/Sentence Fluency—Makes frequent errors in grammar, spelling, mechanics, and usage; sentences run together or are confusing; throughout this piece, the writer has failed to follow the conventions of grammar and mechanics; spelling is at times incoherent.

How I Get Ready for School

I have to get up erly for school every morning. I dont lik getting up erly. This is what we do before we leave the house. First we get tost and eggs most days for brekfest. Mom has brekfest before us some times. Then we have to clean our teeth too. I can walk to school becus its not too far from my house. When its vry cold we put on our shirt and always carry book bags and lunch. We use to take the school bus but now we live close we can walk.

Focus and Coherence—Gives information about a topic, but may stray from focus; the writer has a general focus throughout but strays from it at various points throughout the piece.

Organization—The writer omits a main idea or offers few supporting details.

Development of Ideas/Word Choice—Attempts to develop ideas, but may be inconsistent; the writer develops a topic or two, but generally strays from the concept; chooses words that are often ill-suited for the purpose; in this case the writer has chosen the word *shirt* when the word *coat* would have been appropriate.

Voice—The writer has difficulty expressing an inviting, unique tone.

Conventions/Sentence Fluency—Makes mistakes that can interfere with the reading of the writing; sentences flow in a somewhat fluid manner; while this writer generally focused on the correct topic of getting ready for school, at times the writing was very circular, continually coming back to walking to school, and placing events out of order.

Getting Ready on School Mornings

Here is how I get ready for school on school mornings. We have to get up so erly for school! First, I get up and dress and go down to eat. Next, my dad fixes things we like, espechly eggs or pandcakes. He is a real shef so he knows how to cook lots of good things. All my things fit in my back pak. Last we walk to school with Ann and Tommy from next door who are best friends with us. That is the way it goes every school morning.

Focus and Coherence—Gives information about a central topic; the selection is on a single topic relating to the writing prompt; the writer has provided information and details related specifically to that topic.

Organization—Presents a main idea and supports it with details; the details support the main idea and don't stray very much from it; the sentence "He is a real shef so he knows how to cook lots of good things" strays slightly from the topic.

Development of Ideas/Word Choice—Attempts to develop ideas; uses word choice to suit the purpose; the writer has chosen appropriate language to convey the meaning of their paper.

Voice—The writer uses a personal voice that generally expresses an inviting, unique tone.

Conventions/Sentence Fluency—Spelling, capitalization, punctuation, and usage are mostly correct; sentences lead naturally to those that follow; the writer has some errors in spelling and grammar, but they do not take away from general understanding of the details or topic.

Don't be Late for School!

Thats what my mother says every day becaus I like to be lazy in bed. But in the end I have to get up so I won't miss school. This is how I get ready for school every morning. First I jump up because its late already. Next I eat eggs, cereal with milk or my favorite breakfast which is waffles with honey. Then Mom helps me fix my hair and I bush my teeth on my own. After that I put on my shirt, pants, and coat. I take my book bag and milk money. Last Dad takes me to school in the car. That means I get to nap a little. It is just the same every day but some times Mom or Grandma take me.

Focus and Coherence—Gives interesting and detailed information about a central topic; the writer has a single topic relating to the prompt; the information provided about the topic makes sense and is interesting to read.

Organization—Presents a main idea that is supported by clear, factual details; the details provided support the main idea; the writer does not stray on tangents; from beginning to end, the paper is organized and coherent.

Development of Ideas/Word Choice—Thoroughly develops ideas; uses precise word choice to enhance quality of content; the writer is descriptive without going off topic; the words chosen do not take away from the descriptions, but only help the reader to understand.

Voice—The writer uses a personal voice that adds an inviting, unique tone to the writing.

Conventions/Sentence Fluency—Writing is almost entirely free of mechanical, grammatical, and spelling errors; sentences flow from one to the other; the writer has minimal mistakes in spelling and grammar.

Picnic

Have food lik hot dogs corn sandwiches and grapes. Frens and famly culd come. You culd bring a softball for catching. lakes are nise picnic spot so are they beach when its sunny, If you get a cut. Thats why you brings a first aid kit. Picnics are some my favrit things.

Focus and Coherence—The writer does not give information specific to a central topic; overall, the writing is not coherent.

Organization—Although the writer provides details, they do not combine to support a main idea; the ideas are not arranged in logical order.

Development of Ideas/Word Choice—Provides little or no development of ideas; the writer omits or fails to use chosen words correctly (e.g. "You culd bring a softball for catching").

Voice—The writer does not express a personal voice.

Conventions/Sentence Fluency—Makes frequent errors in grammar, spelling, mechanics, and usage; sentences run together or are confusing (e.g. "Have food lik hot dogs corn sandwiches and grapes").

Planning a Picnic

It is not hard to plan a picnic. First plan what you will have to eat. Hots dogs and sandwich are delishus foods and you don't need forks to eat them. The beach is a fun place so is the lake or a park. The park by me close at sun down. You need to be safety. So bring a bike helmat and first aid. That is how to plan a good picnic for friends and famly. I went to a picnic last year.

Focus and Coherence—The writer gives information about the topic of picnics, but strays from the how-to-plan focus.

Organization—The writer omits a main idea; the details do not add up to support a main idea and are not arranged in logical order (e.g. the last sentence is "I went to a picnic last year").

Development of Ideas/Word Choice—Attempts to develop ideas, but may be inconsistent; the writer chooses words that are often ill-suited for the purpose, as in "you need to be safety."

Voice—The writer has difficulty expressing an inviting, unique tone.

Conventions/Sentence Fluency—Makes mistakes that can interfere with the reading of the writing; sentences flow in a somewhat fluid manner.

A Picnic Plan

Here is how to have a great picnic. Pick some of your favrit foods to bring like hot dogs and corn. I don't like hambergurs too much. Find an open place for you and your frends to run around. That way you can have games. The beach or a lake are good picnic spots. Be safe too when you ride your bike or play. I know somebudy who got hurt on his bike. You could have music too if you or your frends play an instroomant. Or bring a radio for music. Everyone will have a fun time if you plan your picnic well.

Focus and Coherence—The writer gives information about a central topic, picnics; the writing maintains its focus on planning a picnic.

Organization—The writer presents a main idea and supports it with details; occasionally, the writer includes unnecessary details (e.g. "I know somebudy who got hurt on his bike).

Development of Ideas/Word Choice—Attempts to develop ideas; the writer uses word choice to suit the purpose, such as "good picnic spots."

Voice—The writer uses a personal voice that generally expresses an inviting, unique tone.

Conventions/Sentence Fluency—Spelling, capitalization, punctuation, and usage are mostly correct; sentences lead naturally to those that follow.

Unit Assessment

A Wonderful Picnic

If I planned a picnic here is what I would do. I would plan a picnic that is fun and safe. The beach or the park are good places. Kids can play all kinds of games with your friends and family. Hide and seek and catch are exciting games and so is jump rope. My family would bring a baskit with yummy food like sandwiches or hot dogs. I also mite bring a first aid kit for if someone gets hurt. Thats how to have a fun and safe picnic.

Focus and Coherence—The writer gives interesting and detailed information about the central topic, planning a picnic.

Organization—Presents a main idea that is supported by clear, factual details; the ideas are organized in logical order; the writer includes a simple introduction and conclusion.

Development of Ideas/Word Choice—Thoroughly develops ideas; the writer uses precise word choice to enhance quality of content, such as "yummy."

Voice—The writer uses a personal voice that adds an inviting, unique tone to the writing.

Conventions/Sentence Fluency—Writing is almost entirely free of mechanical, grammatical, and spelling errors; sentences flow from one to the other.

Unit 1 Reteaching and Intervention Opportunities

Tested Skills and Strategies	Teacher's Edition-Small Group	Approaching Reproducibles	Practice Book	ELL Resource Book	Intervention Guide
Comprehension Skills					
Author's Purpose, 1	33H, 131R, 131X	46	46	46–53	See Guide
Sequence, 2	61R, 77T, 77Z, 105HH	16, 25	16, 25	16–21, 28–31	See Guide
Character, 4, 9	33R, 33X	6	6	4–9	See Guide
Plot, 6	105R, 105X, 105HH	35	35	34–41	See Guide
Sequence, 8	33R, 33X, 61R, 61X, 77T, 77Z, 105R, 105X, 131R, 131X				See Guide
High-Frequency Words					
very, 5; *too,* 7	61L, 61R	13	13		See Guide
Structural Analysis					
Inflectional Endings -s, 28, 29		4, 14	4, 14	37	See Guide
Double Final Consonants, 3, 30		23	23		See Guide
Literary Elements					
Identify Rhyme, 10, 20	33K	48	48	19	See Guide
Text Features and Study Skills					
Photographs, 11		8	8	10–13	See Guide
Labels, 12		18	18	22–25	See Guide
Lists, 13		38	38	42–43	See Guide
Book Parts, 14		28	28		See Guide
Phonemic Awareness/Phonics					
Phoneme Blending, 19	33W, 77S				See Guide
Phoneme Isolation, 21	33Q				See Guide
Short a, 22, 23	33K, 33Q, 33W, 33CC, 61K, 61Q	1, 11	1, 11		See Guide
Short i, 24	77M, 77S	21	21		See Guide
Consonant Blends, 25, 26, 27	105K, 105Q, 105CC, 131K, 131CC	31	31		See Guide

Language Arts	Grammar Practice Book	TE Unit Writing Process	ELL Practice Book
Grammar, Mechanics, and Usage			
Sentences, 15	1–5		3
Word Order, 16	6–10		7
Capitalization, 17	21–25		19
Punctuation, 18	16–20, 21–25		15

© Macmillan/McGraw-Hill

Unit 2 Reteaching and Intervention Opportunities

Tested Skills and Strategies	Teacher's Edition-Small Group	Approaching Reproducibles	Practice Book	ELL Resource Book	Intervention Guide
Comprehension Skills					
Sequence, 1				62	See Guide
Plot, 2	111R, 111X	85	85		See Guide
Main Idea and Details, 4, 6, 8, 9	35R, 35X, 81T, 81Z	56, 76	56, 76	60–67, 88–91	See Guide
High-Frequency Words					
some, 5; *many*, 7	65L, 65R, 65DD, 81TT, 81Y, 81FF	62, 73	62, 73		See Guide
Structural Analysis					
Contractions, 28, 30		63, 83	62, 83		See Guide
Inflectional Endings, 3, 29		54, 74	54, 74		See Guide
Literary Elements					
Rhythm, 10		58	58	68–71	See Guide
Text Features and Study Skills					
Diagram, 11		68	68	82–85	See Guide
Dictionary, 12		78	78		See Guide
Follow Directions, 13		98	98	114–115	See Guide
Use Photographs, 14		88	88	102–103	See Guide
Phonemic Awareness/Phonics					
Phoneme Isolation, 19	35Q, 35CC, 111K				See Guide
Phoneme Blending, 20, 21	33K, 35W, 65W, 81S, 111W, 141W				See Guide
Short o, 22	33K, 35O, 35W, 35CC	51	51		See Guide
Short e, 23	65K, 65Q, 65W, 65CC	61	61		See Guide
Short u, 24	111K, 111Q, 111C	81	81		See Guide
Consonant Digraphs, 25	141K, 141Q, 141W, 141CC	91	91		See Guide
Consonant Blends 26, 27	81M, 81S, 81Y, 81EE	71	71		See Guide

Language Arts	Grammar Practice Book	TE Unit Writing Process	ELL Practice Book
Grammar, Mechanics, and Usage			
Plural Nouns, 16, 17, 18	31–32, 34–35, 36–40		27, 31
Proper Nouns, 15	41–45, 46–50		35, 39

Unit 3 Reteaching and Intervention Opportunities

Tested Skills and Strategies	Teacher's Edition-Small Group	Approaching Reproducibles	Practice Book	ELL Resource Book	Intervention Guide
Comprehension Skills					
Main Idea and Details, 1	81T, 81Z	125	125	144–147	See Guide
Compare and Contrast, 2	65R, 147R, 147X	146	146	166–175	See Guide
Make and Confirm Predictions, 4	65R, 65X	116	116	132–139	See Guide
Character, 6	115R, 115X, 115 GG	137	137	132–139	See Guide
Sequence, 8	35R				See Guide
Problem and Solution, 9				143	See Guide
High-Frequency Words					
there, 5; more, 7	65L, 65DD	113	113		See Guide
Structural Analysis					
Inflectional Endings, 3, 28, 29, 30		103, 123, 144	103, 123, 144		See Guide
Literary Elements					
Sensory Language, 10		148	148	176–177	See Guide
Text Features and Study Skills					
Floor Plan, 11		138	138		See Guide
Newspapers and Periodicals, 12		128	128		See Guide
Chart, 13		118	118	140–141	See Guide
Signs and Symbols, 14		108	108	128–129	See Guide
Phonemic Awareness/Phonics					
Phoneme Deletion, 19	65Q, 65CC, 147W				See Guide
Phoneme Blending, 20	1Y, 147Q				See Guide
Phoneme Isolation, 21	115Q, 115CC 8				See Guide
Long a, *22*	35K, 35Q, 35W, 35CC	101	101		See Guide
Long i, *23*	65K, 65Q, 65CC	111	111		See Guide
Three-Letter Blends, 24, 27	147K ,147Q, 147CC	141	141		See Guide
Consonant Digraphs, 25, 26	81M, 81S, 81Y, 81EE, 115, CC	121	121		See Guide

Language Arts	Grammar Practice Book	TE Unit Writing Process	ELL Practice Book
Grammar, Mechanics, and Usage			
Present-Tense Verbs, 15, 16, 17	51–52, 54–55, 56–57, 59–60		43, 47, 55
Past-Tense Verbs, 18	61, 65		51

Unit Assessment

Unit 4 Reteaching and Intervention Opportunities

Tested Skills and Strategies	Teacher's Edition-Small Group	Approaching Reproducibles	Practice Book	ELL Resource Book	Intervention Guide
Comprehension Skills					
Problem and Solution, 1	109R, 109X, 109HH	187	187	218, 220, 221	See Guide
Character, 2	65R, 65X, 65HH	165	165	196–205	See Guide
Retell, 4, 11	35R, 35X, 65R, 65X, 81T, 81Z, 109X, 137R, 137X	176	176	210–213, 230–239	See Guide
Main Idea and Details, 6					See Guide
Author's Purpose, 8					See Guide
Vocabulary					
Multiple-Meaning Words, 5		157	157		See Guide
Compound Words, 7		168	168		See Guide
Use a Dictionary, 10		157, 179	157, 179		See Guide
Literary Elements					
Rhythm, 12		204	204	240–241	See Guide
Text Features and Study Skills					
Numbered List, 13		171	171	206–207	See Guide
Telephone Directory, 14		181	181		See Guide
Chart, 15		193	193	192–193	See Guide
Captions, 16		160	160	224–227	See Guide
Phonemic Awareness/Phonics/Structural Analysis					
Phoneme Blending, 21, 22	35W, 81S, 137W				See Guide
Phoneme Addition, 23					See Guide
Long e, 24, 27	65K, 65Q, 65W, 137K	162, 195	162, 195		See Guide
Long o, 25	81M, 81S 81Y, 81EE	173	173		See Guide
Long a, 26, 28	35K, 35Q	151	151		See Guide
Inflectional Endings, 3, 9, 29, 30		156, 189, 200	156, 189, 200		See Guide

Language Arts	Grammar Practice Book	TE Unit Writing Process	ELL Practice Book
Grammar, Mechanics, and Usage			
Commas, 17	93		
Capitalization, 18	88		
Present-Tense Verbs, 19, 20	81–85, 86–90		67, 71
Writing Prompt			
Expository: Persuasive Report		143A–143E	

Unit 5 Reteaching and Intervention Opportunities

Tested Skills and Strategies	Teacher's Edition- Small Group	Approaching Reproducibles	Practice Book	ELL Resource Book	Intervention Guide
Comprehension Skills					
Compare and Contrast, 1	97T, 97Z	231	231	282–285	See Guide
Sequence, 2, 6	125R, 125X, 159R, 159X	242, 253	242, 253	288–295, 302–313	See Guide
Make Inferences, 4	81R, 81X	220	220	268–277	See Guide
Cause and Effect, 8, 11	51R, 51X	209	209	246–261	See Guide
Vocabulary					
Inflectional Endings, 3, 7, 9		211, 223, 245	211, 223, 245		See Guide
Use a Dictionary, 10		212	212		See Guide
Literary Elements					
Alliteration, 12		259	259	314–315	See Guide
Text Features and Study Skills					
Use Photographs and Captions, 13, 14		215	215	262–265	See Guide
Bold Print, 15		226	226	278–279	See Guide
Book Parts, 16		236	236		See Guide
Phonemic Awareness/Phonics/Structural Analysis					
Phoneme Blending, 21, 22	51W, 81W, 97Y, 125W, 159K, 159CC				See Guide
Phoneme Isolation, 23	125Q, 125CC				See Guide
Diphthongs /ou/, 24, 26	125K	239	239		See Guide
r-controlled vowel or, 25	97M, 97S, 97Y	228	228		See Guide
r-controlled vowel ar, 27	81K, 81Q, 81W, 81CC	217	217		See Guide
Diphthongs /oi/, 28	159K, 159Q, 159CC	250	250		See Guide
Abbreviations, 29		222	222		See Guide
Prefixes re- and un-, 30		255	255		See Guide

Language Arts	Grammar Practice Book	TE Unit Writing Process	ELL Practice Book
Grammar, Mechanics, and Usage			
Antonyms, 5	111–112, 114–115,		91
Capitalize Proper Nouns, 17	103, 123		
Prepositions, 18	121–122, 124–125		
Contractions, 19	113, 118		
Adjectives, 20	101–102, 104–105, 106–110		83, 87
Writing Prompt			
Expository: How-to		165A–165E	

© Macmillan/McGraw-Hill

Unit 6 Reteaching and Intervention Opportunities

Tested Skills and Strategies	Teacher's Edition-Small Group	Approaching Reproducibles	Practice Book	ELL Resource Book	Intervention Guide
Comprehension Skills					
Classify and Categorize, 1, 2	97T, 97Z	286	286	354–357	See Guide
Make and Confirm Predictions, 4	135R, 135X	297	297	360–373	See Guide
Fantasy and Reality, 6	41B, 41X	264	264	320–331	See Guide
Make Inferences, 8	81R, 81X	275	275	336–349	See Guide
Character, 11	167R, 167X	308	308	378–389	See Guide
Vocabulary					
Inflectional Endings, 5		300	300		See Guide
Antonyms, 7					See Guide
Context Clues, 9		278	278		See Guide
Use a Dictionary, 10		267, 289	267, 289		See Guide
Literary Elements					
Rhyming Patterns, 12		314	314	390–391	See Guide
Text Features and Study Skills					
Headings, 13, 14		303	303	354–357, 374–375	See Guide
Media and Web Resources, 15		291	291		See Guide
Lists, 16		281	281	350–351	See Guide
Phonemic Awareness/Phonics/Structural Analysis					
Phoneme Isolation, 21, 22	81Q				See Guide
Phoneme Blending, 23	81W, 135W, 167Q				See Guide
Digraphs oo, 24, 26	41K, 41Q, 41W, 41CC	261	261		See Guide
Digraphs /ô/, 25	81K, 81Q, 81W, 81CC	272	272		See Guide
Closed Syllables, 27	135K, 135Q, 135W, 135CC	294	294		See Guide
Final Stable Syllables, 28	167K, 167Q, 167W, 167CC	305	305		See Guide
Possessive Pronouns, 29		277	277		See Guide
Prefixes, 3; *Contractions*, 30		299	299		See Guide

Language Arts	Grammar Practice Book	TE Unit Writing Process	ELL Practice Book
Grammar, Mechanics, and Usage			
Capitalize I, 17	133, 143, 148		115
Pronouns, 18, 20	131–132, 134–135, 136–137, 139–140		107, 111
Subjects and Predicates, 19	126–127, 129–130		103
Writing Prompt			
Expository: Persuasive Report		173A–173E	

Teacher Notes

Teacher Notes

Teacher Notes

Unit Assessment

Teacher Notes

Teacher Notes

Teacher Notes

Teacher Notes